Prologue

February 13, 2009

I've sat on a ledge between sanity and insanity for as long as I recall. One false move and all the king's horses and all the king's men wouldn't be able to put Humpty Dumpty or me back together again. Little did I know today would be that day.

It all began when my unit deployed to set up a mobile command post in support of Operation Phantom Phoenix—a continuing offensive to drop a planned 40,000 pounds of explosive by two B-1 Lancers and four F-16 fighter aircraft on al-Quaeda positions in the Arab Jabour area of Baghdad. It was the third month of my second deployment and my team's three-month rotation when I was briefed along with other non-commissioned officers that we would participate in an operation-based emergency preparedness exercise. I would supervise our replacements in the new mobile command post before passing the baton and rotating back to our base. The airman, seated at the console, was to walk me through each step he would take in real-time if such incidents occurred on his shift.

1

Everything was going according to regulation. Real airplanes were taking off, flying actual sorties, then landing. Men and women with enlisted and officer insignia standing over us watched every move without saying a word but writing notes on their notepads. The young airman correctly flight-followed the aircraft missions, coordinated in-air refueling, and disbursed first responders to the runway where an aircraft with supposed disengaged landing gear prepared to make an emergency landing. With phones ringing, radios screeching orders to aircraft, and ground crews disbursed at time-saving intervals—a simulation began with insurgents attempting to overtake the command post. A real M18-colored smoke grenade was tossed into the room, simulating a biochemical agent. Having trained, each person prepared their M25 chemical warfare mask and placed the mask over their head, pulling it down over their face—all but me. I stood frozen, mask in hand, while the smoke caused my eyes to water and made breathing difficult. I was stunned at my reaction when I thought about what could've happened if it were an actual biochemical agent. I realized my fear of dying was less terrifying than my phobia of suffocating from the mask or being confined in a small space. My supervisor rushed me out into the fresh air as he screamed at me, "I expect this from a newbie, but not an NCO. What the hell is the matter with you, Sergeant?"

"I can't put this over my face. I've never had to." My hand grips my knee as I cough and spit and hold the mask out for him to take. "I've carried it around in my mobility bag for years, and I've never put anything over my face," I managed to sputter. Escorted to sick call and subsequently excused from the rest of the exercise, I didn't understand why I froze in a time of crisis. I did, however, understand the adverse effect refusing to wear the mask had on me physically. Never before had I faced such a dreams, but I knew better. I want to call her and demand answers, but she's never answered my questions honestly. Why would she now?

During my follow-up appointment, Major Smith looks down before speaking. A tell-tale sign I'm not going to like what I'm about to hear. He informs me that my medical file will meet the Medical Evaluation Board to determine if I will be allowed to complete my enlistment. The thought of waiting to find out if I will lose all I have worked for and return to the United States as a civilian, combined with leaving Roland, my boyfriend of six years, paralyzes me with fear. Failure is not an option for me. I have witnessed too much failure, and I am not about to start a downward spiral at twenty-four years old and end up stuck like my mother.

The idea of returning to my dorm feels like returning to the crime scene. Instead, I stop my car at the large field, looking out over the airfield. I've driven by here every day for nearly six years, but this is the first time I've ever taken the time to stop. There is a large boulder; I climb on top of it to watch the airplanes take off and land. It reminds me of another boulder, looking out over a river where I used to sit and contemplate life. Of course, that was six years ago, in another city and another country, where my friend, Tracy, told me of her plans to join the Air Force. The life I imagined back then didn't include staying in my small town. I wanted to attend college, so the military was my best option. I had a curiosity about the world and looked forward to running as fast and far away as possible. I wanted to experience a life free of dysfunction and abuse. At eighteen, I recognized some classmates were ready to vow their lives to one person and marriage. I knew then I wasn't born with that gene. I made a vow, too. I would never allow a man to hurt my child or me. I would never be stuck in a situation and unable to care for myself financially, emotionally, or physically. I would succeed, travel the world, and be kind, especially to those who couldn't protect themselves.

Climbing down from the boulder, I leave with a plan—no matter what the medical board decides, I won't stop searching for the truth. People usually lie for one of two reasons: to protect themselves or the one they're lying to. I want to know whom Sylvia was trying to protect.

Resigned that the future of my military career is no longer in my control, I pack this new depression and anxiety in my overnight bag as mindlessly as my toothbrush. If I am stuck in a holding pattern until the Air Force decides my fate, I will do it, enjoying what time I have left here in the UK. Now, sitting behind the wheel of my hatchback, putting the car in gear, and refusing to look back until the base gates are in the rearview mirror, I barrel south down the A1 toward London. Roland is the only person in this world I trust completely. I push my favorite CD into the player; I'm Like a Bird by Nelly Furtado blares from the speakers, and I extend my arms, impersonating my best bird wings. The irony is overwhelming as it occurs to me; I flew as far as I could from the dysfunction of my family, only for their reach to cross an entire ocean and touch me here.

Three months later, none of my other acts of meritorious service, awarding me with a USAF Commendation Medal and an Achievement Medal, are considered in the Medical Evaluation Board's decision to separate me medically. Something happened during the hypnosis that can't be undone or unseen. What happens next is the impetus for what my life is to become. I'll know the truth no matter the cost.

Chapter 1

Everything I Wanted

May 10th, Present Day

Do you want to know how to kill monsters? Desire nothing, feel nothing, and fear nothing. I used to believe monsters only came out at night, so the darkness frightened me. But that was before discovering monsters live among us; they don't just hide in closets and under beds. They come in the form of everything we want, declaring they love us.

I regain consciousness, not all at once, but one eye at a time —my left and then my right. Confused, I blink several times, attempting to clear the darkness. I try to lift my head, but the pain is excruciating; I immediately imagine a bowling ball whirling down the lane and striking the pins. Panicked and believing the pain in my head has somehow caused me to lose sight, I slide my hand through my hair and find a golf-ball-sized knot beneath a spot of sticky matted hair. I can't see it, but the copper smell tells me it's blood. I slide my hand to the left side of my forehead and follow the stickiness down the side of my face, releasing strands of my hair dried in the blood.

I reach out and touch what is around me, becoming aware of the tingling in my left arm and fingers; I use my right hand to free it before shaking it back to life and stretching both arms out in front of me. A glow of red and green lights shines under the sleeve of my jacket. It's a welcome light in this world of darkness —my watch. Grasping my Garmin watch, I push the button near my right pointer finger, and it offers a dim light. *At least I haven't lost my sight.*

Adjusting my position, I stretch my legs as far as they go until they meet resistance. My imagination conjures the worst scenario and my biggest fear as I suck all the air out of the room and slowly become aware of my predicament. *Breathe.* I focus on how I got here and where I am.

Jane and I arrived at the bridal boutique at the same time for my final wedding gown fitting. While we nibbled fresh fruit, the ladies and I sat on overstuffed duvets, sipped morning champagne, and discussed "l'arte del vestire," the art of dressing.

Later, while standing in front of the ornate mirror, dressed in the white A-line, satin, forever in my heart, plunging and extravagantly expensive gown, the reflection appeared; the room faded into the background, the dress sparkled, but my face was shattered.

Shaken by the vision, or whatever the hell that was, my future mother-in-law and I stopped for a lovely lunch and nibbled on stories faster than our salads as we discussed the loving attributes of one man, her son and my future husband. I described the reflection I saw in the mirror, and she assured me it was just pre-wedding jitters. I accepted her reasoning, not wanting to taint the morning with my mental clutter.

Jane left first; then I headed home only to decide to clear my mind with a walk at the last minute since I had time and hadn't gotten my daily steps in. I was halfway back from the farthest point of the walking trail and approximately half a mile from my car when I experienced a stabbing pain in my lower abdomen, decreasing my pace to a leisurely crawl. Then the rain came. I stopped to untie the arms of my jacket from around my waist and removed my AirPods, suddenly becoming aware of my surroundings. My mind was preoccupied with the pre-wedding to-do list and disturbing vision until I noticed the path was nearly empty of pedestrians other than the man following me.

The huge man with long legs had no reason for the slow crawl he maintained to stay behind me unless it was deliberate. I became highly aware of the predicament I'd let myself get into. The threats and warnings we'd received over the past months immediately became my uppermost thought; I had let my guard down. I pulled my cell phone from my pocket to speed-dial my fiancé, but he didn't answer, so I spoke extremely loud to the voicemail, "I will be home in a bit. I changed my mind and walked the Falkirk to the Kelpies Trail today, but I'm almost back to the car. Yes, I'll...." Even after I heard the beep signaling the end of the allotted time, I continued talking to air the rest of the way back to my car just in case the huge man intended to cause me harm. I picked up my pace as the cramping subsided but kept watch behind me while making a mental note of the man's distinguishing features. He was huge in stature, wearing a gray jogging suit, gray trainers, and a black stocking cap, and he didn't have facial hair.

Finally, I paused to look over my left shoulder near the car park, but the man was gone. I twisted to look over the right; he wasn't there either. He didn't disappear to the right unless he swam across the canal. He had to have exited the path and ventured into the woods to the left. The water dripped off my coat and soaked the car's front seat. I pushed back the hood of my jacket and fumbled to place my water bottle in its holder. I laid my cell phone on the passenger seat beside my purse and on the top of the white garment bag holding my wedding dress. I shook the water from my hands and searched the glove box for something to dry them and my face. Safely locked inside my vehicle, I scanned the car park questioning my paranoia, but I quickly wondered if I had escaped something meant to harm me. I shivered.

The rain stopped. I started the engine and put the car in reverse, moving slightly backward before stomping the brake. I saw someone dart past the rear of the vehicle. When I turned my head to check, I saw a child soaking wet, no more than nine or ten years old, standing at my driver-side door. Believing myself safe, I parked the car and rolled down the window to speak to the crying child who could not find his mum. I shut the engine off and stepped out.

Suddenly, someone behind me put a hand over my mouth. I felt an excruciating pain in my head and heard a crack.

I learned a long time ago to heed warnings. There hadn't been threats for over a month, and I believed myself safe. I dampen my finger with spit and try to rub the dried blood from around the side of my face. Taking a deep breath is painful, like sucking broken glass through a straw. I recognize an anxiety attack and remind myself to take slow breaths. Breathe in through my nose and out my mouth. I stretch my arms up, relieved they only meet space. I begin to stand slowly, unsure how much room is above me. I meet resistance when fully standing erect. I'm 5' 6" with my palms touching the top; I guess whatever I am in is six feet in height. I molest the walls and determine that there are four sides, not round. *Relief.* What is worse than dying? Being placed in a hole and not dying instantly, or perhaps a mask over my face.

I press the button on my watch again, twice. It searches for a GPS signal, so I wait. I have no choice but to wait. It can't retrieve a signal. Where the hell am I?

The first wall is rough, damp, and cold, with ridges my fingers can follow, similar to the pattern I traced on the floor. The second and third walls are not stone; they're not wood, maybe, plaster? They don't feel splintered as I would imagine the inside of a box or crate would feel. I force slow deep breaths at the thought of a box. The fourth side feels like wood. I continue moving my hand down it until I reach a latch, sending relief throughout my entire body. I sigh and carefully attempt to move the latch and open whatever I am inside of, but it doesn't move, as I suspect. My fingers follow along a ridge that takes up much of the wall; it's a door. I place my ear to the door and listen. It is eerily silent as I strain to hear the smallest decibel— nothing—no birds, no wind, no creaking old house, nothing but my labored breathing. I push the button on my watch again.

12%

Tues 10 May

1:30

I blink, still trying to adjust my sight to the inky darkness. Placing my hand in front of my face, I know it's there, but it is invisible to me. Fuck calm; I lift a scream from somewhere deep inside and push it out of my trembling mouth before yelling, "Can anyone hear me? Is anyone there?" I scream again, louder and longer this time. Lightheaded, I kick and pound the door repeatedly until it moves slightly. I know if buried, the sheer weight of dirt would prevent movement. Besides, what is the likelihood I'm buried in a box vertically? My 140 pounds are on my feet, not my backside. Somehow, that knowledge calms me and slows my breathing. I brace my arms against the walls and lower myself to the floor. I slide my boney ass a matter of inches from corner to corner and calculate I'm in a four-foot by four-foot area. I assume a closet. Please, God, not a box.

I'm frightened, to be sure, but it's larger than a coffin-sized box. More so, I'm terrified of what is on the other side of the door. "Let me out. Please, let me out," I scream over and over. Tears begin to stream down my face. I fought them since regaining consciousness, but now I allow them to flow freely. I taste the snot in my mouth before wiping it away with the back-side of my hand. I'm left with the taste of salt from my tears. My breathing is raspy as I place my head in my hands.

I recognize this fear. The darkness is no friend of mine, but I am familiar with him. I inhale deeply, then slowly push the air out repeatedly.

I flinch, startled by the loud roll and clap of thunder above me. After the initial fright, I am grateful for the noise. I am also thankful for my stuffy nose, the smell of my bad breath, and the blood on my forehead as I cover my mouth and nose with one hand while pushing out air, hiding the scent of mold and dirt permeating my nostrils.

I've held the urge to pee since I woke. What do I do now? I don't want to soil my clothing; who knows how long I'd have to sit in it? I hold it until I can no longer hold it, and the pain reminds me of the pain in my abdomen that slowed my walk while the man followed me. I remove my shoes, leggings, and underwear, then slide my feet back in my shoes before I squat. It's not like I haven't squatted before, but that was while road tripping with my girlfriends and a case of beer, and I wasn't three months pregnant.

The urine spatters above my shoe and ankles; it feels hot on my cold skin. I tap the floor as cautiously as I would a hot stove to see if I've flooded the floor below me. The puddle follows gravity, spilling itself under the door to my relief. Redressed, I lower myself down to my knees and prepare to pray. Looking up, I wonder if God knows who I am. I haven't exactly lived my life for Him. I've prayed my entire life except when I was on my way to sin. Maybe that counts for something. If there is any time I need a prayer answered, it is now. "Lord,...if not for me, please protect my unborn child."

After what felt like hours, I abruptly stopped praying and sat on the floor, becoming as small as possible by pulling into myself; I know how to do this. Now, propped in the corner with my legs up around my belly as far as my baby bump will allow, I rest my head on my legs.

With no more tears to cry or prayers to pray, I flip the imaginary book in my mind over to the cover, verifying this isn't my story. My story isn't over until the last paragraph, the last sentence, even the last word. Besides, I write my story.

Unlike the vision in my hypnosis or the reflection, I wasn't pushed, nor did I fall from the summit of my life; no, not me. I nosedived into this bottomless hell when I sought out and demanded the truth before writing and then publishing my novel, *Daddy Issues*. Was the truth worth the cost, Dahlia?

Chapter 2

Whisky Girl

January 14th, Four Months Prior

The driver opens my door, and while stepping out, I smooth the creases in my cream-colored Dolce & Gabbana pencil skirt and pull my coat tightly around me. When last in London, nearly thirteen years ago, the Shard didn't stand as the tallest building in the UK, and even if it had, I couldn't have afforded to stay at the Shangri-La.

Upon entering the lobby, I stand and admire its beauty, looking like the tourist I am, when two women approach me. A tall woman dressed all in blue and wearing too much perfume places her right arm around my waist and snaps a photo. I'm not sure which happened first, the sneeze or the blinding flash of light. Laughing loudly, the woman looks at the picture she just took as I dig in my bag for a Kleenex. She turns the phone around, pushes it closer to my face, and says, "Oh, look. That won't do. We need to take another." I sneeze again.

"Dahlia Frost, would you mind taking a photo with us?" the shorter dark-haired woman asks in her American accent as she now approaches her taller friend, whose unnecessary flash blinded me.

"Back away, Barb, and give Dahlia some space. Crowds are not her thing, remember? Didn't you read the same book I did?"

Smiling at the shorter woman, I think I like her very much. "Of course. We all three need to be in it—and prepared," I reply.

The taller woman, Barb, stops an elderly couple and asks the woman to take our photo. "Of course. Is she someone famous?" the older woman asks.

"Oh, yes, Dahlia Frost is the author of *Daddy Issues*," Barb replies and grins as she moves to my left side. The shorter woman moves to my right. The older woman snaps our photo and hands the phone back to Barb. Then the elderly woman, who only seconds ago didn't know who I was, hands her husband her phone and steps to my right side as her husband says, "Cheese."

"We're in London for your book signing. I can't believe our good luck staying at the same hotel," the shorter woman informs me.

"Amazing, that is lucky. I will see you both at the signing tomorrow." Walking away quickly, shrills of delight startle me. Turning, I see the same two women taking photos with a tall man. He turns too quickly, preventing me from seeing his face, but there is something vaguely familiar about him. How he stands and holds himself reminds me of someone I used to know. My steps quicken to reach the lift; now a safe distance away, I glance over my shoulder, hoping to verify the man's identity, but the two women, the man, and the crowd around them are gone. While I take steps to enter the opening doors, my efforts are thwarted after a child in front of me spills his bag of round, multi-colored candies on the floor.

I stand frozen as the sound of pebble candies bounces off

the marble floors. The young boy drops to his knees, trying to gather the bouncing pieces and knocking into me at shin level. I regain my balance, sigh loudly, and watch his mother reach for him. The vast room closes in on me, and I feel hot. I fan my face and pull the collar of my blouse away from my neck. Needing space and air, I lift my arms and outstretch them to elbow distance to regain my personal space. The boy's mother tugs on his puny arm to pull him up, and I attempt to step backward and out of the way.

A man's voice from behind me speaks, "Pardon me," with a very familiar soft Scottish accent.

Only minutes after, I hear a female voice, "May we take a photo?" I wait to see if she is speaking to me. I have no intention of turning around to see to whom she speaks.

The last fifteen minutes have been a live version of a pinball game, hitting a bumper to my left, slingshotting across the field to hit a bumper on my right, then catapulting again. I stop the madness by stepping off to the left without looking behind me and cutting in front of several other people patiently waiting for a neighboring lift. Safely hidden, I don't dare turn around and face the doors until they close, but I'm curious to get a glimpse of the man. I see the back of the tall man's wavy blond hair. I shrug and mouth the words, "I'm sorry," to the faces that found my action rude. I truly am sorry but have no intention of bumping into the man from my past if he is, in fact, Roland. The calm demeanor I pride myself on disguises my quickened heartbeat, sweaty palms, and quivering legs. It won't heighten my image if people see the woman who wrote about facing our truths head-on is videoed running from her past.

As the lift rises to the 48th floor, my thoughts teeter between possible and impossible, eventually landing on the impossible. It can't be. It isn't. When I step into my hotel room, convinced it isn't him, I quickly direct my attention to the floor-to-ceiling windows overlooking the river Thames. The view does not disappoint. The windows span a 180-degree view, including the Tower of London and Tower Bridge. Taking a few deep breaths, I place my palms against the glass to watch the lights of the city's boats, buses, and cars going about their business.

I welcome the travel-size bottle of whiskey I find in the minibar. It isn't until my stomach growls that I feel the pangs of hunger and place my dinner order with room service. I rearrange the couch to look over the city before sitting back, drinking my dram, and kicking off my favorite red pair of Louboutins. Better.

I turn the hot water on in the shower creating a sauna before stepping in to scrub off the last eighteen hours. It's not until I step out naked and dripping wet that I am haunted by an image staring back at me that I no longer recognize—too thin, drunk, and a broken young woman filled with self-pity and about to self-destruct. The image fades to the overweight woman free of alcohol but swallowing her fears. Both these versions of Dahlia Frost hated their lives and were in a constant battle for my ass to get over it, on with it, and do something more. I remembered what I wanted and strived for when I was in the military. It was then that I realized my success was on the other side of my fear, so I sat down at my computer and became a writer. Writing replaced breakfast, lunch, dinner, movies, company, and some-times even showers. The hours spent writing masked the loneli-ness I created with my choices.

I swipe my hand over the mirror, wiping away the steam and images. Now I see a healthy, fit, wealthy, and successful woman staring at me. *There I am.*

Now, sipping my second dram of whiskey and devouring the shepherd's pie I ordered from the menu, I allow myself thir-teen minutes to think of Roland, an equal number of minutes to years since I last saw him. Just the thought of him has my nerves sizzling and must be the reason for my flashbacks and anxiety.

I question whether it was him I saw in the lobby, and if so, what are the chances I would run into him at a hotel. Last I knew, he lived in London. I am sure of one thing; if it's him, he isn't sitting in his hotel room eating dinner alone or thinking about me. My self-loathing drunk girl raises her head. *You have issues.* I silence her and quickly offer a rebuttal as I finish the second dram. *I may have, but one of them is not whiskey.* I have a strong like for the taste of whiskey and the warmth that coats my throat. It feels like a hug as it goes down. What I have is an emotional attachment.

Curling up on the king-size bed with a full stomach, about to doze off, I reach for the remote to turn off the television when I glance at the screen and see his face. Instead of turning it off, I sit up and turn up the volume. I'll be damned. He did it. Frustrated that I have any type of reaction, I press the off button on the remote to quiet the noise in the room and immediately wish I had a remote to quiet the noise in my head. I'm haunted by memories most days, but I have needed an exorcist since arriving in London.

Waiting for sleep to come, I'm startled by the loud ring of my cell phone. "Hello, Charlotte." My business partner, best friend, agent, and chosen sister doesn't let me get too far without checking in.

"Hi. We finally arrived and checked in. Our flight was awful. How was your flight?"

"My flight was fine. What happened with yours?" I hesitate before continuing and rapidly confessing, "Charlotte, I'm not sure I can do this."

"We flew through storms, and oh no, you don't. You have to do this. You can't hide behind the pandemic anymore."

"I'm not trying to hide. I didn't expect to be recognized first thing after I arrived. It was the first time I wished I was wearing a mask. After we published *Daddy Issues*, the pandemic and lockdowns afforded me the luxury of being Frances Slater. Now, here I am about to put myself out there for the world to meet Frances Slater, but instead, fans are meeting Dahlia Frost, and I'm surrounded by speculation. I thought the best part of us owning our publishing company was making the rules. I thought I would go unrecognized promoting the novel in the UK as a virtual unknown."

"Dahlia, there is no way you or I could have guessed how well the novel would do. You have devoted fans. You need to get out there and meet them. Look at it this way. You've been on the best seller lists for nearly a year, given several over-the-phone interviews, and nothing catastrophic has happened. It's getting made into a movie. Your name and face were bound to be publicized eventually. You have nothing to worry about." Charlotte's voice is consoling. "Right? Believe me; this is for the best. Get a good night's sleep. We'll see you in the morning."

The following morning, waking early and dressed for a run, I make my way from the hotel to the Gherkin Building, then the Square Mile, and back. As my running shoes pound the concrete, I try to outrun the thoughts in my head and ponder what Charlotte said last night. She is right. I need to embrace this new me; friendly, outgoing, world-traveler, and author.

Two hours later, Charlotte and I make our way to the lobby and out to the waiting car. I am relieved to see Jamie, the publishing company publicist, in the vehicle. The SUV passes by the front entrance of Waterstones as I push all the air out of my lungs and twist my neck as far as it will go, "Who the hell sent out posters with my photo?" Reading the poster in the storefront windows, *Daddy Issues,* photo op, and book signing with *New York Times* best-selling author Frances Slater, I say, "It has my photo on it. No wonder the women recognized me."

"I had them made up and sent them out once you agreed to do the book tour, per Charlotte's instructions," Jamie answers.

"I wish I'd have known ahead of time." I sigh wearily and shake my head. Out of the corner of my eye, I watch Jamie shrug at Charlotte, and in turn, she waves it off. I'm not trying to be difficult, but neither of them knows what I go through, how debilitating PTSD and anxiety can be.

Continuing around to the rear of the store, Charlotte and Jamie exit the vehicle leaving me alone with my thoughts. I sit and savor the vehicle's protection a bit longer. I expected to feel nervous but terrified better describes the shaking, nausea, and shortness of breath I am currently experiencing. I inhale and exhale deeply. What the hell did I expect? The novel is popular and has created a following of devoted readers that love the characters Emma and Joshua. Of course, people will be showing up to my first book signing. People have been traveling as much as possible since the ban on flying has lifted.

I thought I arrived early enough to familiarize myself with the surroundings and devise an exit strategy. I can't change my mind even if I want to; I need to do my part since I privately funded the publishing company. Charlotte and I have gone all out and used my novel as a major promotion. The company poured money into advertising and promotion to generate maximum sales profits. I'm not in the habit of losing money.

Entering through the rear door, I'm escorted to a waiting room. I sit for a few brief minutes in an overstuffed chair and make myself comfortable. I slip off my shoes, pull my legs under me, and sip my Diet Dr. Pepper and whiskey from my flask. I stare at the flask as I take a sip and calm my nerves. It's better than any VA-prescribed Xanax. Now I'm in control of the memories. Good memories associated with the smell of whiskey and Roland replaced the disgusting memories of my stepfather's breath. I now associate the smell of whiskey with love and warmth, not stench and vileness. I take another sip of courage.

"Frances Slater, author of *Daddy Issues*." Even before hearing my introduction, I fix my line of sight on the chair where I am to sit. Once safely behind the signing table, enjoying the false sense of security it provides, I quickly scan the room and establish an escape route. I've always stood out in a crowd, which isn't necessarily good. I can't understand why. So, for years, I have strived to remain invisible, and now I am out here for the entire world to see. Why did I do this to myself?

My head snaps to the left as I notice Roland's face on a stack of books sitting to the right of my signing table. If I had time, I would dwell on that, but I don't; instead, I am handed a copy of my book and begin to greet fans, sign an equal number of autographs, and smile.

The second woman approaches the table and hands me her novel. "Hello, Dahlia. It is so nice to meet you." The petite woman with brown hair and eyes extends her hand to shake mine as she continues, "I flew to London because I want to be one of the first fans you meet at your first book signing. I wouldn't have missed this opportunity." The woman is a bit older than I am, I guess. Her words are quick and accent thick. I hear a smile within them. It's infectious. I try not to stare at the scar across her face. She points to it. "Your honesty and the deeply personal stories about yourself and your mother's own experiences are what finally helped me to leave my abusive husband. He cut my face years before, yet I stayed with him. How sad is that? But, after I read your book, I realized I wasn't going to be stuck either. I left and have never looked back. Now the scar is a reminder of what I won't allow."

If I could cry, then surely it would happen right now. Moving around to the other side of the table, I hug her. She squeezes me before we take several photos together. This is the moment I realize it is a good thing readers know my real name and that my stories and Mom's are true. Each copy I autograph represents a story of someone being saved from abuse, running from abuse, or grateful for the honesty and information about where to get help.

Charlotte and Jamie smile from the corner of the room while holding up two thumbs. The room is still crowded after an hour when Jamie allows readers to buy merchandise and hand out contact cards for the international charity we founded for abused children and adults. With a sense of relief and accomplishment, a smile crosses my lips as I exit the store area to take a short break and be alone for a few minutes. I'm overwhelmed by the number of stories shared with me and how sharing our stories helped so many.

In the waiting room, I wipe the sweat from my hands before reaching for my Diet Dr. Pepper. Noticing a bottle of whiskey, I pick it up and read it. It isn't until I see the name on the bottle, Whisky Girl, that I am confused. It wasn't here an hour ago. The question is, how did it get here? I google the brand Whisky Girl; I gasp and cover my mouth as it occurs to me who owns the company and that this isn't a coincidence. Sticking my head around the door, I motion for Charlotte. As I point toward the whiskey bottle, she follows me into the room, "Do you know what that is?"

"It's a bottle of whiskey. How did it get here?"

"I want to know if you brought this for me."

"No. I've never seen it. Why?"

"Please find out where it came from." My hands are visibly shaking when I point toward the bottle. Roland is near. Not knowing how I will react if I see him scares me.

I hear Charlotte's voice as she approaches the room after tracking someone down to ask, "Excuse me, can you tell me where this bottle of whiskey came from?"

"It was delivered for Ms. Frost with instructions to put it with her requested Diet Dr. Pepper. It is sealed; I checked it myself. Is everything fine?"

Stepping out of the room, I ask, "Yes. Did a man drop it off?'

"No, it was a runner. I accepted it and signed for it myself."

"Thank you, but did it come with a card or a note?" I ask, and the woman shakes her head no.

Charlotte enters the room, shrugs, and holds up a thumb. I nod. I don't have time to explain who makes this whiskey. I hold up my thumb, and she disappears back to the store. Spooked but grateful, I uncork the bottle and pour a dram. I don't care where it came from as I sniff the dram and pick up on the nose just as Roland taught me. I enjoy the flavors of peach, apricot, honey, and butterscotch as it warms and soothes my throat and nerves. I love the taste. Roland is in London and knows where I am. Of that, I am sure. If it were him yesterday, did he see me? I don't want to see him.

I'm ready to put myself back out in the crowd and begin autographing, taking photos, and listening to many tales of heroism. I am amazed at the stories they share, and I'm proud of the book, even if writing under a pseudonym to protect the identities of my mother and me.

Suddenly, the room explodes in cheers as people clap loudly. When I raise my head from the book's pages, most guests face the store entrance instead of the signing table. I stand to see, but the crowd of people, the layout of the store, and the placement of bookshelves prevent it. Immediately, I am in fight or flight mode and consider putting the escape plan into use. Looking to my left, I see the door that exits to the hall, which leads to the outside door I entered when I arrived. Charlotte and I meet eyes, and she steps toward me, pointing toward the door. She knows I'm good at controlling my issues in a typical environment but not so much in a crowd of people.

Determined to see this through, I stretch on my tippy-toes, and over the top of the heads of all the guests, I see the same familiar man I thought I saw at the hotel only yesterday. He is six feet two inches tall with broad shoulders and, by sheer size, demands space. This man is larger than life. His blond curly hair, square-shaped jawline, and blue eyes are hard to forget, but his smile is unnerving. It makes my heart stop, if only for a second, and I must remind it to beat again. I watch him walk toward me, dressed in black jeans, a white t-shirt, and a black leather jacket that fits him very well. I try to hold his stare, but I can't help but notice his long muscular legs. Instantly, I compare his image to the one burned into my memory. I brace myself by hanging on; maybe the table will break my fall if I pass out.

Oh my God, Charles Roland Hughes, I did see him. He's older, more muscular, and his long curls replaced with more of a military cut. Time has been kind to him. I can't believe he is here. Frantically, I turn my back to him. *What should I do? I can't stand with my back to the crowd forever. I can run, but how would that look?* I blow all the air out of my lungs before I choose to face the past. I turn around, staring at his huge smile as it inches closer. I'll be damned if he sees me run. I'm not the same twenty-four-year-old woman he last saw and kissed goodbye at the airport. Instead, I am standing frozen in front of him with trembling hands and weak legs, acting like a teenager. I've not progressed. I know exactly how long it's been since I last saw this man, twelve years, eight months, and eight days.

Being in London might be a coincidence, but at the same hotel and bookstore, I think not.

I deliberately stare into his smoldering blue eyes, watching him make his way to the front of the crowd, in front of the table, and directly in front of me. He winks and grins. His large hands and long fingers pick up a copy of *Daddy Issues*, flip through its pages, and place the book down in front of me, "Dahlia." My name rolls off his tongue, and I stare at his mouth as he speaks it. He continues, "Would you autograph my copy, Dahlia Frost, please?" pointing to a spot on the page.

I am staring into his eyes.

Quit staring at him.

The chatter in the room assaults my ears, and the smell of Roland's cologne evokes memories of when he and I first met. As the room stands still, I drift off in the memory of when we met, another time he walked toward me. He had nowhere to go as I knocked into him, and with such force, if he had not wrapped his arms around me, I would've fallen backward. I placed my hands on his chest, looked up, and stared into the bluest eyes I'd ever seen; he smelled so good.

"Please, autograph right here," he whispers again in his alluring accent, bringing me back to my present state of adoration. I pry my eyes away, look down where he is pointing, and scan the page, page 143; the heat rises in my face as I recognize it as a love scene between my two main characters, Emma and Joshua.

Thankful to sit down and stop my legs from shaking, I autograph where he is pointing. I watch his every move as he moves around the table, but disbelief glues me to my seat. His long fingers reach for my hands, and his two strong arms pull me up to meet him. The memory of his touch scorches my senses. Although I hear the crowd, which reminds me, they are there and watching, I only see him.

He smiles from ear to ear as he pulls me into a tighter hug than it should be, and my body quivers, betraying me, and I know he feels it too. When he lets go, I immediately step back and assume my intimidating pose, hands-on-hips, and a resting bitch face. I wish he weren't smiling that seductive smile as I remind myself that I don't like this man, not one bit. He's lucky there is a crowd of people to watch our reunion.

The movement around me, the clapping and whistling, brings me to the present. I am surprised by the reaction of all the women in the room. I've never witnessed anything like it in person until now—women swooning as far as my eyes can see as they snap photos of him or fervently type on their cell phones. I can only assume they are texting their other female friends, letting them know Roland Hughes' current location—a bat signal, so to speak.

Turning my attention to him, I don't offer a greeting. "What are you doing here?"

He grins and holds my hand, "What do you think I am doing here?" He pauses just long enough for my mind to jump to several conclusions, all of which make me uncomfortable.

"I pay attention to my social media accounts. I happened to see a tweet cross my feed about an author I recently stumbled across and began following being in London for a book signing. Imagine my surprise to learn that Frances Slater and Dahlia Frost are the same people. It is the perfect opportunity to kill two birds with one stone."

"Two birds, one stone. What does that mean?" I can't hide or control my body's physical reaction to him, but I don't need to be happy about his grand entrance, and I don't hide it in my tone.

"One, you've evaded me for nearly thirteen years, and what are the chances of both of us being in London at the same time? Two, I popped in to do a secret signing of my new book. I am taking advantage of my good luck." He picks up one of his books and shows me.

I don't believe it is just good luck.

The line is long, and I hear the whispers of a few women in the front. One asks, "Will you both read the passages of *Daddy Issues* from the pages Roland asked you to sign? Joshua's character is obviously based on Roland and Emma on you."

The stone walls of fiction I carefully placed to guard my non-fictional life were already breached when my real name leaked, but Roland's appearance used a wrecking ball to finish the job.

Quietly I answer, "Is it? I can't. I am sorry." I watch the woman look from me to Roland as if he will help her. He stands up and places his hands on his hips, egging this on.

"Will you read the passages you just autographed for Roland, please?" a different fan asks.

"I can't do that. I think that is a bad idea."

"She can do it." He begins clapping, sits back down, and opens his copy of my book. "I'd be happy to oblige."

Looking at the crowd, I can see women's heads bobbing up and down as they stand on their tippy-toes, trying to get a better view of him. The women in front are still snapping photos, running their hands through their hair, touching their faces, and adjusting their clothing.

I've been in worse situations, but none so desperately that I want to run away. I lean into Roland and whisper, "I can't do this."

"Yes, you can. You wrote it based on a memory of us. Read it to me." He leans in and whispers in my ear, "Guess who was cast for the role of Joshua."

"What? No one told me they found my Joshua." I speak louder than I intended and quickly turn my head to see his expression. His hot breath in my ear and proximity are causing me to melt. This is ridiculous. I am a grown, successful woman.

"Well, they found your Roland." He smirks at me and presses his palms down to spread out the pages of my book. He prepares to read for the audience.

"Well, they found your Roland," I childishly mock him under my breath before picking up a folded piece of paper to fan my face. How many times can a person's heart stop in just two days? I am sure I have reached my limit. I knew I should've used my exit plan. Damn him. I turn the book to the pages I'd written about Roland and me, a.k.a. Joshua and Emma, based on the memory of one particular evening in Edinburgh. I glance at Charlotte, and everything she is thinking is transparent on her face. Even I blush.

Staring down at the pages, I read quietly at first until asked to read louder. *"At the touch of Joshua's mouth, Emma's body felt it was on fire, and she was burning alive. She reached for something to hang onto; as he backed her against the wall, she found balance, placed her hands behind his neck, and pulled him toward her."* I quit reading aloud, pausing for Roland to continue. He tips my head up and my face toward him. He isn't reading from the pages—double damn him. Roland looks into my eyes and quotes the paragraph from page 143. *"He wanted her. Joshua kissed her deeply, crushing his body to hers. He pinned her to the wall, hands above her head, and braced her with his knee. Making love tonight was not an option. If forced to say goodbye tomorrow, tonight would be about pure burning and primal need for both of them."* He quits speaking and grins at me. I plead with my eyes to end my suffering. Roland doesn't continue reading; instead, he states, "What a descriptive scene for your two fictional characters. That is what great writers do."

The women are clapping and staring at him while I watch them. I can see what they are thinking; each woman imagines she is with him as described in the book. As I told in my novel, I remember the night of our non-fictional lovemaking. All I want to do is crawl away, and he loves every bit of it.

I quickly motion for the next woman in line to move up and get her autograph. After I sign, I watch as the woman turns to page 143, pointing for him to autograph her copy in the same place I autographed his. Then she picks up his book, and he autographs it, and she moves to his side to take a photo with him. I notice more women piling into the store and realize this will be an all-day event. We sign many more books, and I call for another break—a well-deserved break after hours of signing, smiling, and posing.

Standing, I turn to walk away and immediately make my way to the whiskey to pour myself a second dram and calm my severed nerves. Then I pour him a dram. I'd pinch myself, but no need; I know my senses are all working and on overload. I turn and lean against the buffet-type table with a drink in each shaky hand. He enters moments behind me and takes the drink while scanning my body, eventually meeting my eyes.

"Do I make you nervous? Slainte Mhath," he toasts. "You used to appreciate whiskey as much as I do, Whisky Girl." His voice is shaky, and I don't miss the chance to revel in his moment of discomfort. He doesn't know how I will act now that we're alone and out of the public eye. Maybe he isn't quite as cocky when in private. He grins, dragging me into a memory of how my nickname came about.

"You do remember when you were my Whisky Girl, right? When I found out you were in the city and at this bookstore, I couldn't help myself. You're not mad, are you?" Roland turns away from me and glances around the room, waiting for my response.

"I remember what I used to be," I answer sharply. I remember everything, and I don't need reminding. "Mad isn't the word for how I feel. Confused, Roland, I am confused about why you would come here today and send a bottle of whiskey before your arrival? A warning, perhaps that I failed to heed? Maybe if I had known of your success, I would've suspected you were about to hijack my book signing. That is something the Roland I knew would do." I step away from the table and toward the chair.

"I thought we might need something to relax the nerves a

wee bit, lighten the mood. I thought it would be a nice peace offering. Do you remember me telling you that whiskey arouses an emotional reaction? Whiskey was the best peace offering I could bring you. It's tied up in our story."

"Yes, it is indeed, and so are a few other things. Do you plan on shocking me with them as well? I don't know what to say. Never in a million years would I have thought I would run into you while in London, let alone my book signing."

"You didn't run into me; I purposely collided with you this time." He smiles, knowing I will catch his meaning. He is such a player. He is so good at this. He steps closer to me; I watch his lips tighten into a scowl, "Where have you been the last thirteen years? And why didn't you answer any of my phone calls or reach out to me?"

Standing guarded, I hold my ground and place my hands on my hips. Roland doesn't know me anymore, but I am sure he knows what his closeness is doing to me; it's intimidating. My breath is labored, my mind racing and my entire body quivers. Tears take me unaware; they fill my eyes and form in the back of my throat. I can't remember the last time I cried. Oh, yes, I do, and it was over him. It took a very long time to get my emotions under control after his betrayal and the hypnosis, but when I did, I quit allowing any feelings until right now. It can't be him that makes me feel again—it can't.

I knew the moment I collided with him all those years ago and touched his heart that I would never love another, but then again, I love with a passion, and I hate with a passion. There is a very fine line between the two. I've gone thirteen years believing I hate this man, but now that he is touching me, I realize I'm a fool for thinking I had forgotten or was over him. That is all the more reason to send him far away. I can't ever be foolish enough to believe a word he says again.

"Let's finish here and go have dinner."

I want to believe his sincerity until it occurs to me that Roland is an actor, and this is what he does. "No, I can't." I step out of his arms and back under my shield of protection.

"Why not?"

"How is it that you reach out to me after nearly thirteen years? Why would you assume I want anything to do with you after the Dear Jane letter you sent?"

He searches for his next words carefully. I stand still and search for changes in his expression. His arrogance rears its head as he whips around and appears shocked that I would refuse him. It occurs to me that I am supposed to be like all of those star-struck women in the other room. He forgets I know the real him. At least I used to, and that is the Roland I can't trust.

"I received a Dear John letter from you. I thought you wanted nothing to do with me. I didn't write you a Dear Jane letter. What are you talking about?"

With the wind knocked out of me, I gasped. He jerks his head toward me, and I know he heard the air escape me. *Did I misjudge you?* I didn't intend to speak those words aloud. I regress, "Really?" I stare at him and pause for a brief minute before I rudely ask, "Why don't I believe you, Roland?"

I know why I don't believe him. He is a man, and I don't trust any of them. And my desire for control overrules my desire for intimacy and close relationships. I want to believe him. I want to believe that if he tells me the sky is falling, I could trust him enough not to have to look up. I trusted him like that once, which proved to be an error.

"Answer this. Suppose I wanted to end things with you in a Dear Jane letter, tell me why I would call you every day twice a day for two months after receiving your Dear John letter? Let me remind you that you didn't answer even one of my calls or letters." He talks with his hands and steps closer.

I need to deescalate this now, so I abruptly agree. "Okay. We can discuss this further over dinner. I'll give you that much because I know how often you called and wrote even though I never read your letters. Besides, I have questions, and I want closure." I blot my eyes and face trying not to smear my makeup. He places his hand on the small of my back, leading me, and I'm positive he remembers what that slight yet intimate gesture means to me. I look down, not at him, definitely not at him. Whatever ice surrounds my heart for this man just melts, but I can't show him that. If he didn't write the letter, then who did? I need to know. As we enter the area to sign more autographs, I whisper, "I'm staying at the Shangri-La."

"I'm staying there as well. We are meant to be Whisky Girl, then and now."

"Yes, I know. I saw you when I checked in."

"And you didn't speak to me? That's cold."

"You have no idea, Roland."

Chapter 3

All The Whisky In The World

Looking out over the city, I contemplate standing Roland up until the scent of him surrounds me; his cologne and the feel of his touch hijack my thoughts. Pulling my shirt up to my nose, I inhale the intoxicating mashup of blackcurrant, Italian bergamot, and oak of his cologne left behind when he pulled me close. I'm not sure I want to rehash the past. Being near him is a temptation I can't allow, but I need answers if I want to leave this city with a greater understanding of why things happened the way they did.

"Hello," I answer my hotel phone and sigh loudly after hearing his displeasure with my tardiness. "Look, Roland, have you seen all the photos and social media posts from just the short time we were together today? I don't want any more attention paid to us."

"Aye, but I've not seen anything concerning, and I'm the one sitting in the hotel restaurant and bar scrolling through my phone while looking like a man who's been stood up."

"You're not going to let me pass on dinner, are you?" I pause, waiting for an answer, but I only hear silence before saying, "It's just dinner. I'll be right down." When I reach the restaurant, he stands and pulls out my chair. Once seated, I hold up my phone and ask, "How do you deal with the notifications and comments?"

He points toward my cell phone. "You need to mute it," he instructs me. "Take my advice and don't read the comments. They won't all be nice, I warn you."

"Oh, I will. This phone has not stopped notifying me since fans posted the first photos. Celebrity is your thing, not mine. Roland, listen to this comment posted to a photo of you and me once you reached the signing table. You're smiling from ear to ear, and I look like I've seen a ghost. Well, I had, actually." Reaching across the table to tap his hand and get his attention, forgetting I already had it before being swept up in the comments. I see he's smiling at my hand on his, so I pull it away. "I'm sorry." I glance into his eyes, swallow hard, then continue, "It reads, 'Ex-military, huh? She looks easy enough to kill.'"

His eyes widen. "I'm sorry. I can't control what other people write. I would if I could believe me."

"I realize that, but my true identity reveal was a small leak compared to your grand entrance and the chaos it is creating. I want no part of this. My desire to be loved and adored has a limit. I had no idea you were acting or have such a following until today."

"You truly have been in hiding, haven't you?" His face is hidden behind his menu, "Let's order. I am famished." Roland changes the subject. I mute my phone and lay it aside. We look like an ordinary couple, except he appears to be the picture of health, and since my return to London, I'm once again the damaged young woman he took to the distilleries and dared not to fear the smell of whiskey. I take a large sip of my whiskey— neat to prove to myself I am most definitely not she. We sit across the table, looking over the city to avoid staring at each other. "Beautiful, isn't it?" He asks.

"It's a beautiful view. I love seeing all the lights. When I checked in last night and thought I saw you, I wondered if you were out there. It comforted me to think you were down there somewhere, and you were. I am still shocked we are both in London at the same time."

It's hard to remain a bitch, keep a straight face and not laugh when he begins retelling stories of good times we shared years ago; riding motorbikes, attending the Air Force ball, attending theater performances, and teaching me to drive on the opposite side of the road. He even adds the sound effects of grinding the gears. "I know how to drive a stick, Roland. I was scared of driving on the opposite side, not to mention the roundabouts at such high speeds. Okay, what about you at the distilleries? You would've thought it was Christmas."

"The hangovers not so much. But at least I wasn't sick for days. You, however, were rubbish."

"Well, in all fairness, you were teaching me to disassociate the abuse from the smell. How else could I have learned?" The easiness between us came naturally. What started as friends quickly became friends with benefits and grew into love once he taught me how to love him in return. I had to let go of control and allow intimacy. He taught me how to trust a man and build a relationship. I believed it would last a lifetime, evidenced by how we still seem to know each other so well after not speaking in years. We were once the same; what we like to drink, eat, listen to, activities, and even how we want to shut the world out and be alone in our heads once in a while. That's how we Tauruses stay connected to the earth and grounded as we dream of flying to the moon. He appears to be reading my mind and peering into my soul when I glance at him. I break the spell and look away, realizing our conversation is laced with politeness and memories of only the good times, but it can't stay this way. I have little time in London, and now that he has crashed into my life, I want to know why, and I want to know who wrote the letter if he didn't. When he speaks next, the spell is broken.

"Let's talk about our trip to Edinburgh since you brought it up and wrote about it," he suggests. I can feel the change in the mood instantly. What was surrounded by nostalgia is now clouded over in mistrust.

"Why not? I love dinner and a movie. Moving on to the entertainment portion of tonight, right? You start." I speak the words yet dare him to begin.

He smirks, "Dinner and a movie. That's cracking." He sips his drink and looks around the room. "I took you to Edinburgh because I wanted time with you away from what you were going through and privacy away from our friends. I introduced you to my mother and brother because I needed to know if we had what it would take to withstand a long-distance relationship and if we had a future. I believed we wanted the same things."

"I thought we wanted the same things too. After the medical board determined I would be medically retired and PCS back to the US, I left believing we'd only be apart a few months. Then, I received the Dear Jane letter a month later. It was a hard time in my life."

"Mine too. It's not like my life went on happily without you."

"It appears it did." I wave my hand at his life now.

"You have no idea how thrilled I was to discover you were only minutes away from me today. I knew it could go one of two ways, but I was willing to take the chance." Roland sips his drink.

"I am flattered you took the chance, especially after

witnessing what kind of media frenzy you stir up. I didn't know what to think or do when I saw you. My first reaction was to run."

"I knew you would want to run, and when you turned your back to me, I thought you were doing just that. I do remember that about you. I thought I knew you better, but it wasn't until I read your novel that I fully saw you on the page, a woman desperate to do and be better than her mother—a woman struggling to find and fight for answers so she can slay her monsters." He smiles and waves at someone. I stare out over the city's lights for an extended time, trying to decide what amount of added information I am willing to share with him if any, but he's a man on a mission and has something to say. "I have to say," he says, and I smirk at his words. It seems he has a lot to say. He continues, "I was pleased to learn you discovered what memories were missing from your childhood, but I was shocked to read you were kidnapped as a child and nearly drowned. You told me about your abuse, but it wasn't until I saw it on paper that I realized its severity. You aren't so different from the girl I used to know. I felt every emotion come off the page as you described your truth. Truth is important."

Fidgeting with my glass, napkin, and dessert fork, I glance around the room, which is hushed, even with all the diners seated around us. Roland is focused on me and our conversation and oblivious to all the eyes on him. I stop fidgeting and sit up straighter, leaning toward him. "My standard response is that my story is a true one of sinking before I learned to swim. Literally, huh? I wrote the book for my own mental well-being. I always kept a record or a journal of my feelings and experiences growing up. The journal was the only place I felt I could keep my thoughts and emotions safe. I continued to journal after the hypnosis, especially after you broke my heart."

D.F. Kennedy

Roland interrupts, "I didn't write the letter." His expression is stern.

The waiter arrives at our table with our entrees and two more drinks. I sip my whiskey, cut into my bloody steak, and watch him cringe. That was so fun to watch; I do it again. I'm laughing on the inside and find joy in his discomfort.

"I know that now, but I didn't at the time. Anyway, I needed to heal. After begging Sylvia for five years to tell me what was missing from my memories, she finally did, and my journal entries led to writing *Daddy Issues*. I wrestled with the cost of telling a story that wasn't entirely mine alone to tell, but the decision paid off. Sylvia told me there is a cost for the truth, but I'm also aware of its value."

Roland leans toward me; he reaches out and holds my hand lying on the table. "If we're going to talk, let's not dance around our truth. Frankly, I don't have time for it. As you just said, there is a cost to the truth. I didn't just seek you out today because I wanted to see you. I also have questions."

I pull my hand out of his and cut more of my steak. There is a lull in the conversation as we eat our food. I can hear an imaginary drum roll, just waiting for what he has to say, but I'm ready because that means this night will be over. "Go ahead. That's why we're here, and I have a few questions of my own."

"I didn't know that you were even pregnant until I read your fucking novel. I want to know why that was," he declares louder than he should as his smile turns to that same tight-lipped scowl. I feel the blood drain from my face, and I look around the room to see if anyone is listening or watching us before my glare dares him to discuss this with me. Roland sets his fork down and picks up his glass to take a drink while looking over the rim, "Did I strike a nerve, Whisky Girl? Your intimidation stare doesn't scare me, love. Yes, let's tell the truth." He sets his glass down a

40

bit harder than I believe he intended. "Don't you think you owed me a call, a letter, or something?"

I jerk my head up immediately, "I don't owe you a damn thing." I place my napkin on the table and stand slowly. "Thank you for dinner, Roland." I don't look back at him, leaving him sitting alone at his table with what he thinks I owe him. "Asshole," I say the word to myself out loud as I take the lift back up to my room.

Twenty minutes later, when I answer my door, it is him. "Walk with me to my room, please?" I stare at him. He asks again, "Please, we need to talk." I will regret it if I don't close this chapter of my life while I have a chance, so I follow him, knowing I would be angry if I discovered something like that in a novel.

Sitting at the table in his room, he sets a bottle of whiskey between us, hands me an empty dram, and pours us some liquid courage. The conversation starts friendly but takes on a serious tone again, and I remind myself why I allow him to be near me, let alone spend my evening with him. I know any more whiskey, and I might forget I don't like him.

"Tell me, why did you get angry? Because you think I wrote you a Dear Jane letter? Or because I dare question why you didn't bother to tell me you were pregnant or miscarried? I already told you I didn't write the damn letter, but even if I had, don't you think I should've known you were pregnant with my child and not found out about it in your novel. All you would've had to do is pick up the phone once. Do you know I was going to ask you to marry me when I took you to Edinburgh?" Roland's face is stern.

I pause and think about what he just said before replying, "I don't believe you. I don't believe anything you've said. I didn't believe you deserved to know anything about me or our child."

"Why? When have I ever lied to you? As a matter of fact, when have I ever been anything but kind to you?" He asks.

"Other than when you dumped me in a letter right before I found out I was pregnant?"

"For the last time, I didn't write the fucking letter. I told you I received a letter from you. I'm not taking the blame for what happened to us."

"I want to believe you, but I don't know if I can. I became a reflection of how I was treated, Roland. You knew this about me. You helped me expect more from the people I allowed in my life. The six years we spent together were the best years of my life. I chose you because you made me feel wanted and, above all else, loved. You chose me for the same reasons, didn't you?

"You know I did, Whisky Girl."

"You kissed all my scars away and made me trust you. That hurt the worst—I didn't see your attack coming. There isn't enough whiskey in the world to fix what you broke inside me."

"I guess it's a damn good thing I own a whiskey company then," he fires back at me.

Crying, I sit my glass down and push out of my chair, intending to leave his room, but realize my cell phone and room key are still lying on the table, so I make a quick right into the bathroom. "A sperm donor does not a father make. Is this why you sought me out, to admonish me?" I try to slam the bathroom door, but he follows close behind me and puts his hand up to stop me.

"You believe me, or you wouldn't be here," he says as I whip the door open and try to step around him, but he pulls me into his arms. I attempt to pull away because this fight is useless. Fighting won't get us anywhere. I remember that much. I'm quicker to fly off the handle and get over it, but he is slow to anger and holds onto it like the first pound he ever made.

"Oh, you think you're funny," I say sarcastically.

"One of us needs to be. We aren't going to get anywhere fighting, and that last comment about being a sperm donor is a fine line you just crossed. You didn't give me a choice; remember that." He lets go abruptly and turns his back to me.

Sitting back down, we continue talking, but it is stilted and forced. "Roland, this isn't going to work. I'm not the same girl. I regret that I didn't take any of your calls. I am sorry that I didn't tell you about the pregnancy or the miscarriage and that you had to read about it in the book, but frankly, I didn't think you'd read it or even know I'd written a book. How did you find me?"

"A little over a year ago, I received a call from my brother, Paul, telling me that my sister-in-law, an avid reader, was reading a book by a new author. I wasn't quite sure what interest that was to me until he said, 'When the character described in the book brought you to the imagination of not only her but her entire book club, I read the description as well and thought the writer was indeed describing you and our family.' I asked who the author was, and Paul told me a complicated story that I didn't completely understand; how he had to dig and search through old websites and email addresses, but eventually, a photo of you popped up, and your real name. He remembered when I took you to Edinburgh to meet my family."

"Really? I'd have never guessed that. Look, I'd like to pretend none of these things matter anymore; however, it does, and I have to be honest and tell you the pains from the past are gone, but the scars are not. If you didn't write the Dear Jane letter that led to my spiraling out of control for years, then who did?" I turn back to face the window.

"Listen, love, I don't know, and I don't think we can fix it all tonight." He looks at me through the reflection in the window while I'm trying to find a way to tell him I need to go. I need the conversation to be over and time to process everything we've discussed, but instead, Roland pulls me into his arms. "Dahlia," he speaks my name as if it is a question all by itself before continuing, "If you looked for me, you would've discovered I wasn't hard to find. I find it hard to believe you didn't know I was an actor, but that doesn't matter now. We have another shot at getting this right, and I don't want to mess it up by using the wrong words, and you think it comes from one of my movies. Please hear me out." I nod, and he continues, "There was a time in my career I almost gave up, but I didn't because it was what I wanted to do. I put in the hard work required. How much more time and hard work do you think I would dedicate to someone I love? I never considered giving up on us, not even for a second. So yes, it will work. We both have to want it."

I shock myself when I stretch up and lightly press my lips to his instead of just saying goodnight and turning to go. The tug of war we've participated in all day ends.

"Do you want me to kiss you?" he asks. At that moment, I realize there's nothing I want more. I feel flush, and it's not just from the whiskey. He kisses me passionately, leaving no room for doubt that he loves me and wants me. I relax into him. "It'll take years of sipping whiskey for us to tell each other everything." He says as he searches for answers and reasons.

"Not everything, only the important things," I reply while I finish the last bit of whiskey in my glass and roll it around on my tongue. I'm unsure if I'm tasting hope for a future or regret from the past.

"You would be surprised how much I know about you. Once I found you, I haven't missed much. I searched for you," he adds.

"Really? Well, let's hope it was worth your time and that time heals all wounds."

He lifts my chin. "I know firsthand it doesn't. Someday, I'd like to know why you married another man, considering your actions show you are still in love with me?"

"That's arrogant of you, don't you think? Maybe I am just pretending to care so I can hear all your stories and sell them to a tabloid. Maybe I am just horny."

He frowns and lifts his eyebrows, "Well, I am happy to oblige you, especially after chasing you to London."

"I knew this wasn't a coincidence. I'm unclear what you want from this, especially with our careers, Roland, but I'm willing to be a friend. I don't want frenzied. Your visibility would push me off the ledge I balance on every day."

He frowns and hesitantly adds, "Too late for that. You've already had a taste of what the comments will be. Are you ready for that? Every time we are spotted together, there will be photos and comments. Whenever we are spotted with someone else, there will be rumors of cheating and broken hearts. Again, check your social pages, but don't kill the messenger."

I retrieve my phone and scan my author pages, Twitter, Instagram, and Facebook. Our faces are everywhere. "Roland, you need to read the newest comments."

"Don't read them. I'm serious. Acknowledge them for what they are and let it go. Some will be wonderful, and some will give you the chills. I just want you to be prepared. My advice is to do like I do. Don't read them."

"Listen to this. 'She isn't pretty enough for him. Who does she think she is? Do you think they're just friends? Please tell me they're just friends.' All these comments are coming from a username of forevermrshughes. She is the one who commented I look easy to kill. This type of visibility is what I don't want. I realize we are in an era of social media, which has changed people's ideas and beliefs about privacy. People are braver to say things they might not say to someone's face because they post it to a faceless world, usually without consequence."

"I agree. I want you, and I want us, but you need to enter a relationship with me fully aware of what to expect." Roland lays his phone on the table, stands up, and stretches.

I tell him, "I get it. Your success and life have been open for the entire population to see. I'm sorry, but my relationship with the world is for my work, but any personal relationship has to be about my heart and future." I yawn and wipe away tears of exhaustion. "I supposed even if we remain friends, I will be subjected to the comments."

"Yes, but your popularity is exploding on social media. Haven't you seen it? How many followers did you have a week ago compared to after your name leaked? How many followers have you gained since the first photo of you and me?"

"I don't have a personal social media presence, only Frances Slater's author page."

"Well, check your author page. You need to get prepared."

I can't help but yawn; it's been a long emotional day, and we've said all there is to say. "It's late, Roland. I'm going back to my room."

He escorts me back to my hotel room, and before I open my door, he braces each hand against the wall on each side of my head, leans in, and kisses me.

When he comes up for air, it is as if he is saying goodbye, not goodnight. When I can breathe again, I ask, "Want to have breakfast in the morning?" I'm not ready to say goodbye.

* * *

We have a late breakfast and spend the day together, determined not to let the public decide what relationship we can have. The damage has already been done; how bad can it be? One hour later, he opens the passenger door to his Audi R8, and I slide in. He bends his large frame across mine as he buckles me into the seat, then kisses my lips as he backs out. He tells me, "Hold on, love." When he puts the car in gear and takes off, I feel the power beneath me and the rumble of the exhaust. He drives us to our old hangouts, including the pub he used to work in, where he and I first met. The day starts there but consists of quick stops all over London. He smiles for photo ops around the city while I enjoy watching him interact with his fans.

"It's my turn."

"Your turn to what?"

"Drive."

The look on his face is priceless. I can hear the alarm bells going off in his head as he contemplates whether to let this woman, who is used to driving on the opposite side of the road, drive his Audi. He smiles an unsure smile, and I know I am right, so I add, "If you remember correctly, Roland, I used to drive to London every weekend to see you. It's been a while, but I am sure I can manage." He finally agrees after I assure him if I totaled his car, I can afford to buy him a new one if we survive. He smirks and submits to both our competitive natures. I laugh, recalling the first time I sat behind the wheel and drove on the opposite side of the road. I was eighteen years old and had only been in England for weeks. Since I was a bit of a daredevil, I thoroughly enjoyed the new experience until I approached my first roundabout on the A1. The small villages didn't scare me, but the sheer speed I entered the roundabouts and lack of knowledge of where to slingshot off frightened me.

As I shift into gear, my stomach has butterflies, and I pull away from the pub. I have two things on my list: fish and chips and admiring the London skyline and architecture. We agree to go where the memories take us the rest of the day. It's never too early for fish and chips or pubs in London. My kind of place. Driving with no particular path in mind and no schedule to keep, we leave the city and go to RAF Wittering. When first stationed in England, I spent time with my supervisor and friend, Donna, and her family instead of in my dorm room. We often ate at the little fish and chips shop and visited the local pub in the morning after we learned it closed in the afternoons so patrons would go home and eat. Where Donna and Chris once lived on Boxer Road still looks the same as before when Roland and I visited.

"Do you remember us coming here for dinner with Donna and Chris?"

"I do. Chris and I drank a lot of whiskies together. He was a great guy. Did you keep in touch with them?"

"No, but I wish I would have."

We head south to London; I pass Huntingdon station and point in its direction. "I took many a train ride to visit with you."

"I can see why after seeing how you drive."

"What? What's wrong with my driving?"

"Nothing except you have a heavy foot." He smiles.

Since we have an hour before reaching London, I take it upon myself to ask the one question I have seen on all his fan sites. "I read you've never been married, but what about serious relationships?"

"Never married. I've had a few relationships, but nothing serious." He answers, and I smile internally. He says, "Let me ask you a question. Have you really never watched or heard of the television series I star in?"

"I haven't; I'm sorry. But after seeing all the tagged photos of us together, I scrolled through your social media accounts, and I know about it now. Tell me more about it?"

"No. You need to watch it and let me know what you think," he whispers and leans toward me, gripping my hand to hold.

I laugh. "Okay, I will." Then I pause, "Thank you for 'colliding' into me. I truly believed I hated you until you called me Whisky Girl again."

He faces me and smiles, "Hated me? You will always be my Whisky Girl. I knew I'd find you again; it was inevitable."

"Did you think you'd find me within your millions of fans? I'm sure we all look alike."

"That's rubbish. You are different from my fans. I have everything I need now. Fame can be a lonely life. I am always on guard wherever I go, whatever I do, and what I say. Do women love me? Why? They don't know me. An actress once said, 'Men go to bed with Gilda, but awaken with me.' Do you know it?"

"Yes, I've read it. It was Rita Hayworth."

"I love the fans. I love my life, especially with you back in it. It feels like it has all come full circle, from where we started."

We continue on our driving tour around London and enjoy the landscape and skyscrapers, old and new. I notice there aren't as many as in New York, but the architecture in London amazes me. Pulling into the car park, I grab my visitor's guide before we take off on foot to take photos. "I don't believe you need that visitor's guide. I think I know this city." I smile and feel a bit silly. We take selfies in front of my favorite buildings, the walkie-talkie and the cheese grater, to post them on Instagram and Twitter. We walk past the Gherkin building, located in the square miles. Back at the car, Roland drives. He drives us by the Royal Court Theatre, where he performed. He pulls into the car park near the pub where he worked and the flat where he lived when we first met and fell in love.

"I remember Sloane Square vividly." I blush as I tell him and am reminded of all the time we spent together all those years ago. Arriving at the hotel late in the evening, we continued our visit in my room. He glances at his phone early in the morning to check the time. I take that as my cue, "I have to fly out early this morning, but I enjoyed seeing you again. I am happy you came to London to see me, and I'm grateful we got to talk. I feel we were able to work through everything except the Dear Jane and John letters, but after thirteen years, I don't see how we'll know who sent the letters or why. My letter was typewritten. Was yours?" I ask him.

"Yes, mine was too. It's been too long, and I don't think we'll ever know who wrote them. I'm just happy we found each other again." He places one arm under my knees and one around my waist, picking me up from the chair and carrying me to the bed.

"We can't, Roland." He sets my feet on the floor and gently releases me to stand before the bed. "I can only be a friend for now," I whisper. He kisses me again, and I kiss him back with caution. He unbuttons my blouse, letting it fall to the floor, and I don't stop him. He unbuttons my slacks, allowing them to slide to the floor. He picks me up and holds me against him as he lays me on the bed. I suck in my breath when his fingers touch my neck. As he leans over me, I absorb him; each sense, his beauty, his smell, hearing him breathe, and tasting his lips. He removes his shirt and jeans but leaves his boxers. Sex is not what this is about tonight.

He pulls me into his arms, "I just want to hold you. Is that all right?"

I position myself on my elbow and face him. I explore the exposed parts of his body as I run my hand over him gently as if I've never seen him before with my eyes but am learning every inch of his body from my touch. I stop and place my palm over his heart. "How's your heart?" I ask him.

"It's fine; what do you mean?"

"How's the condition of your heart, Roland?" I whisper. I grasp his palm and place it over my heart, pressing it firmly into my chest. "My heart has never beat stronger or been healthier. I can't risk it broken again."

"I swear, I won't hurt you," he answers me sleepily.

I whisper, "I can't give you my heart, and I don't want the responsibility of having yours."

He pulls me into his arms again. "Good thing I enjoy a challenge. Please, be here when I wake up."

"I'm not going anywhere. Now that we've found each other, I promise I won't, at least until I fly out this afternoon. I can't promise anything else."

Chapter 4

If I Can Make It Here

January 24th

Immediately, I questioned the time spent with Roland, not because I didn't enjoy every second of it, but because of the photos and comments all over the Internet. This morning, I woke to another comment posted from the username forevermrshughes, "Bitch has to die."

I've barely had a chance to breathe since returning home to New York a week ago. My time has been filled telling my story the way I want it told, squelching the rumors and speculation created by the social media posts of several thousand of Roland Hughes' three-point-seven-million followers. My hesitation in answering the rumors was squashed when people presumed to guess why I would choose to write under a pen name. Were the stories I told true or false? Before my London trip, my name leaked to the media was unexpected, but Roland's impromptu hijacking of my book signing shined a national spotlight on me and my novel. Our time together after the book signing only added fuel to the flame.

I check my appearance one last time, adjusting the stray red curl that chooses to be the escapee today. I worked hard for this success, and it is here whether I'm prepared for it or not. Initially, I just wanted to tell the story of my mother and me, often sabotaging my own peace in the process, but I will not allow that this time. No one but the woman staring back at me in the mirror knows all my demons, so I will embrace these changes and recognize them for what they are, a blessing. After the book signing and hearing the stories of the people that *Daddy Issues* has inspired has given me a new outlook; I am ready for my story, my identity, to be out in the universe. I try to pin up the wayward curl one more time. I twist left then right, admiring my new dress and heels before stepping onto the elevator. The elevator chimes as it reaches the lobby, and before my heel touches the marble floor, I tuck the insecure child-like woman away. I held on to her for years since I never had an opportunity to be her, but now I must let her go.

Charlotte and a woman, I am assuming is the new external publicist hired to manage my public image, approach me.

"Good morning, ladies," I say.

"Good morning, Dahlia, I'd like to introduce Olivia Fleming, your new publicist," Charlotte advises me.

"Nice to meet you, Olivia. Are you ready for this?" I ask as I shake her hand.

"Yes, I believe so." Olivia has a firm handshake and an English accent. I like both.

"Try to keep up, and don't let Charlotte or myself intimidate you. If you have read the last magazine article about our publishing company and me, apparently, we are quite a force to be reckoned with. And if you haven't read it, please do so. It is a thorough, and accurate article that was well written." I walk away as I am talking.

"Are you ready to go? Nervous?" Charlotte asks. I first met Charlotte Moore immediately after moving to New York. She and I both lived in the same dumpy apartment building in Manhattanville. She was finishing her MFA at Yale, and I still struggled to find out who I was. She impressed me. After finishing my bachelor's degree, I arrived in New York with only what fit in my car, a stack of journals, and the desire to write and publish. A year later, I began querying agents. Then I received a visit from a man dressed in an expensive designer suit who talked my mother out of my address. He had urgent business to discuss with me. It turned out it was the business of an inheritance, a huge inheritance. When the funds were released, I privately funded and began my own publishing company and partnered with Charlotte. I saw her step into her God-given talent, so I stood back and watched as she snapped her fingers to hurry others along to get the job done. In her early thirties, she is blonde and of average height and build. She may have her MFA from Yale, but I believe her degree is from the school of "I want it, and I want it now." Her energy matches my own. There are very few people I trust; she is one.

"Nervous isn't the word for how my body is reacting right now. But I'm as ready as I'm going to be."

"The SUV is waiting." Charlotte motions.

As we pull up to West 44th Street and Broadway in Manhattan, a building I am familiar with, it's surreal to see the spectators waiting to greet me and get autographs and photos. I stood where the spectators stood many times, wanting to be on the other side of the railing. I had to work hard on the novel and myself. After the initial shock of receiving a large inheritance wore off, Charlotte and I moved out of our studio apartments, which almost cost my entire veteran's disability check. I bought a penthouse apartment on 57th Street overlooking Central Park on the Upper Westside of Manhattan. Charlotte insisted on getting her own place; she maintained living together would ruin our friendship. I have been able to keep my inheritance hidden from the public eye. My mother, Charlotte, and I are the only ones who know that fact other than my attorney, or at least we were. It won't shock me if it is revealed today in my first national television interview. Ginger is known to do her homework.

I wipe the sweat from my palms as I run them down the sides of my dress. I hear Olivia, "The show has 3.5 million viewers. By the time this interview is over, not only will your readers know your name, but everyone who watches television will."

"Three-point five million viewers will be watching me," I whisper. I stand tall, square my shoulders, take a deep breath, and walk in like I have done this a thousand times. I hear the sound of not only mine but Olivia and Charlotte's heels clicking across the floor, reminding me of the day I realized I didn't want just to write; I wanted to publish.

I watched a stunningly dressed woman walk by me wearing a designer suit. But the red stilettos with the red soles captured my attention. I didn't know who or what Christian Louboutin was, but sitting on the bench in SoHo, I promised myself I would one day have those shoes and be that woman. She radiated confidence, power, and money. I longed to be the woman other women would model themselves after, not necessarily in dress or success, but in survival. I am definitely a model of survival and have that mastered. I worked hard for what I achieved—not bad for a young girl who didn't have shoes at one point in her life. After years of rejections, I have earned the reward. After all, Sylvia lived to tell her story, and I lived to tell mine and hers.

* * *

An assistant greets me, leads me to the set during a commercial break, and after a microphone is clipped to my dress, I hear, "Three, two, one," as someone on the stage counts down. "Good morning and welcome. Today, we are joined by author Frances Slater to discuss her novel, *Daddy Issues*, number one on *The New York Times* Best Seller list." Ginger turns her head to face me, "Good morning. It is nice to meet you and place a face to the author of *Daddy Issues*. First, let me ask, is it right to call you Dahlia Frost?"

"Good morning, Ginger. Let me first say it is great to be here. And, yes, of course, it is." Thrilled to be sitting where I am, I release a nervous giggle but quickly scold myself. "I wrote under a pen name to protect my and my mother's identity, but that is a moot point now. If you've read my novel, I am sure you will agree it is a deeply personal story, with a sensitive subject matter wrapped up in an amazing but tragic love story." I smile and gesture to the host to continue.

"*Daddy Issues* was an overnight success and has been a best-seller since its release. The pandemic didn't seem to slow down its popularity. I have been extremely interested in Frances Slater's career and followed her success. You have given numerous magazine interviews and done several podcasts. Today, however, since you are live on the show, I'd like to discuss your novel, which is based on your life and has put a face to the 'Halsey heiress.'" She pauses, "With your permission, I'd like to refresh the memories of our viewers of the media frenzy five years ago."

I nod my head yes.

Ginger continues, "I remember the story very well. As a news correspondent, I am thrilled to reveal the conclusion of that story. Six years ago, the matriarch of the largest greeting card company in the world, the Halsey Greeting Company, passed, leaving only one surviving heir, and no one knew where she was, so the search began and ended with you."

"Yes, that is correct. I had no idea I was the 'Halsey heiress' as the media deemed me. You can understand how I wouldn't have known if you'd read my novel. If you haven't read it, I strongly suggest you buy a copy so you can put the pieces of this puzzle together." I laugh now that I feel more comfortable in front of the camera and the subject matter. "I would like to add that I had already completed my novel before finding out about the inheritance, and I wanted to publish under my own merit. This novel is based not only on my life but my mother's life, and I didn't want those years mistaken for privileged because, again, if you've read the novel, you know there was nothing privileged about it."

"The recent publicity has only fueled the overwhelming interest in the book and, frankly, in Dahlia Frost. Fans fell in love with the characters in your novel, me included. Recently, the novel has created a buzz. Would you like to comment on that and tell us about your book?"

I adjust in my chair and begin, "While in the Air Force, hypnosis reveals something dark happened to a young Emma that prevents her from wearing a gas mask and remaining in the military. Emma returns to the United States to her hometown to find the truth. She suffered a traumatic event that left her with no memory of six years of her life. She also discovers some things are better left buried."

"Your novel is filled with mystery, romance, and amazing love scenes. Inquiring minds want to know anything you can tell our viewers."

"I'm afraid I have nothing juicy to tell you, but nice try," I add, joking with the host.

"We understand the character of Joshua is based on your past real-life relationship with Roland Hughes and that you were reunited recently in London. How are you adjusting to the media attention associated with that and your overwhelming success?"

"I guess you could say Roland and I knew each other back when. We are just friends, and it was nice to catch up with him again. I am thrilled the novel has done so well but showing my face and being in public is terrifying. I decided that if my face and words were paired, I wanted to tell it. I'm a private person and knew it could open a curtain to my world when I wrote and published the book." I continue, "This story begged to be told. I hoped it would help others cope with their traumatic events. I started a nonprofit charity to assist those dealing with some if not all of the same types of traumas. I believe you have phone numbers, websites, and email addresses to give to viewers who may need to reach out for help across the United States."

"That is amazing, and the numbers are at the bottom of your screen." She turns her attention away from the teleprompter and back to me. "I researched your nonprofit before you came here today, and I was amazed to find out your charity has donated millions. Thank you, Dahlia Frost, for joining us this morning, and congratulations on your success." Ginger holds up a copy of *Daddy Issues*.

I hold my breath as they cut to commercial, then Olivia and Charlotte lead me out of the building. "You're a natural on camera, Dahlia. You look beautiful," Olivia says.

"Sure, I'm a natural; I thought I would lose my breakfast on camera." When I step outside, I welcome the slap of the cold January wind on my face as it chills me and stops the suffocating feeling. I shake hands and genuinely smile as fans hold up their cell phone cameras, ready to take photos. I lean over the railings so the fans can get pictures with me in the best possible frame before snapping the picture. I know the images will be all over social media before reaching my next appointment this afternoon.

The SUV pulls up to the curb of the small bookstore; the first thing I notice is the life-size cardboard standee of myself and the same poster I saw at Waterstones. Greeted by the staff, I am escorted to a small room to wait. The room is well lit and smells of old books, candles, and nostalgia. I sit in a rocking chair, place my feet on the ottoman, and make myself comfortable. Today, I am grateful I arrived early. I do as I always do, familiarize myself with the building layout, and plot an escape plan if needed. I have a few minutes to sip my Diet Dr. Pepper and whiskey before my name is announced. I am more relaxed now that I have made several appearances. My thoughts drift to Roland. His "Whisky Girl," I shake my head and relax into how much I miss him. After my name is announced, I read a section of my book aloud, sign and autograph copies, and smile for a hundred photos. I am again amazed at the many stories of heroism.

"Will Roland be joining you for your book signings here in the US like he did when he surprised you in London?" The question isn't what concerns me. My name and novel are now associated with Roland and his fan base; his celebrity status attached to my book bothers me. It is assumed we are a couple, and we are not.

So, I respond the only way I know how. "Mr. Hughes has many projects going and is very busy." I pause. "Thank you for coming, and I hope you enjoy the read."

With the interview and book signing ruled a success, I asked Charlotte and Olivia to let me take them to a late lunch and early dinner at what has become my new favorite restaurant. Immediately after exiting the SUV and entering, Olivia holds her hand up to block the paparazzi. The clicking of the mirror moving each time the shutter is pressed on each camera by the camerapersons is unnerving, not to mention all of them calling out my name. The maître d' seats us in the back corner at my request.

"All right, I'm happy everyone knows who you are, and the novel's a success, but what the hell is the deal with the paparazzi all of a sudden?" Charlotte asks.

Shocked because this has never happened to me, I wonder the same thing and can only assume it has to do with Roland and the "Halsey heiress" reveal. "You know this has little to do with the novel and more to do with the Halsey heiress finally showing her face, and that face has been all over social media with Roland Hughes. It's mostly because of him; I am sure of that. I hope it goes away soon. I can't understand what the interest is in me and what I am eating, though." I point outside to the photographers. Looking around at the other patrons who pay no attention to me or my table allows me to relax, hence, my new favorite restaurant.

Charlotte sits her iced tea down and lifts her hand to wave for the waiter, "I may need something stronger if I'm to hear juicy details. I've repeatedly asked you to tell me what happened in London after the book signing this past week."

"They're not juicy details," I add.

"We need drinks; I'll have a Manhattan," Charlotte says as she points to me.

"Why not? I've already had two. Give me a dram of your finest scotch and a Diet Dr. Pepper. We're celebrating, right?" I point to Olivia, who doesn't look shocked, just confused.

"I'll have a pint, please," Olivia replies to the waiter. This is the first opportunity I've had to look at her. She is taller than me. I'm going to guess 5'8" and weighs maybe 140 pounds. She has beautiful dark brown hair and brown eyes. I put the conversation on hold until we finish the first round of drinks, then I begin. Charlotte tells the waiter to keep the drinks coming.

The Truth

"Charlotte, this isn't that bad of news. I needed time and privacy until I was ready." I say, "Olivia, I had Charlotte hire you for this reason. I need a separate publicist from the publishing company to handle these things."

Olivia nods her head in agreement. "What types of things? What is it you're anticipating?"

"Truthfully, I'm not sure. I've never had to concern myself with this before. I only know I was relieved that this morning's questions or comments didn't blindside me. I trust you will make sure I'm not. I don't know what it is, but something is building; I can feel it. I want to be prepared for whatever it is. I learned to pay attention to the noise long ago, and it's getting loud in my world. Those types of things and handling the positive publicity and keeping the negative publicity away from me. Don't suppose you can do anything about the paparazzi, huh?" I smile. She doesn't seem to have a sense of humor.

"I thought your maiden name was Frost," Olivia states.

"It is. After my father passed away, my mother changed her last name and mine to Frost," I answer.

"Of course, I have read the novel, but I didn't know what the real last name of your father was. Now I understand it to be Halsey," Olivia comments and takes a sip of her drink before continuing, "I wondered where your wealth came from. Charlotte advised me that *Daddy Issues* is semi-autobiographical, and nothing hints at money in that story. This explains a lot. Catch me up on the story if I'm to scramble to handle the publicity over this."

"My father was an only child and died in an accident when I was young. His parents were extremely wealthy. I never had a relationship with them, but before my Grandmother Halsey passed away, she began a search for her last known heir. It created a frenzy across the US, as some news occasionally does. I had no idea I was that granddaughter until an attorney found my mother, and she directed him to me. He contacted me, and I made sure my name was never attached to the news frenzy until I was ready, which is now."

We enjoy our dinner, and Charlotte directs our conversation back to the topic of Roland. "Okay, I want to hear about Roland. Neither Jamie nor I could believe what was happening when he walked into the bookstore. Of course, I knew who he was, but never in the six years I have known you did you ever divulge that the ex-boyfriend who broke your heart was Roland Hughes."

For Olivia, I recap the entire story of what occurred in London. "I believed Roland was the spawn from hell for years," I tell them.

"And now? What do you believe now?" Charlotte asks me.

"I don't know, but he's not from hell because I've been there. I'm far from perfect, and I don't think reconciliation is a good idea, even though I loved seeing him again and realizing my heart wasn't a solid block of ice," I share.

"Sounds like you know what you believe. Maybe you just don't want to accept it," Olivia offers her opinion after she finishes chewing another bite of her salad.

"What I know is, I want to know who wrote the Dear Jane and John letters. I can't fully trust Roland until I know for sure."

"That's so screwed up. How will you go about finding out, Dahlia?" Charlotte asks me.

I take a deep breath, unsure what else they want to hear or how much I want to share. "Seems I have a more pressing mystery than the letters. For instance, who is forevermrshughes, and why does she leave threatening comments on all the photos of Roland and me? If we decide to see each other again, we'll have more time to figure out who would've done it. We didn't dive too deep into the past and just enjoyed catching up after;

we said a few choice words. You saw all the photos, I am sure. That's where we left it."

"If? You've got to be kidding. I am still pissed that every time we discussed your ex-boyfriend, your lost love, you did not mention it happened to be Roland Hughes. Olivia, you've heard of Roland Hughes?"

"Yes, I know who he is," Olivia answers.

"So where exactly did you leave it, Dahlia?" Charlotte asks.

"Good question. I didn't mention it, Charlotte, because I had no clue he'd become a famous actor. You wouldn't have known my ex-boyfriend, so why mention a name? Now, it appears Roland is larger than life. Apparently, you two are familiar with him and his work."

Simultaneously, Charlotte and Olivia gasp before saying, "You've got to be kidding me. You have to watch the series." I laugh and take note of how their faces lit up.

"Really? It must be good. Charlotte, you know I only watch Jax. That would be like cheating." I laugh, realizing I verbalized my crush on a fictional character.

Charlotte hangs her head and sighs before saying, "Dahlia, that series ended years ago; you need to move on. And who better to move on with, Roland Hughes, on your television screen and off. You realize he is the most eligible bachelor in the world."

"Okay. Well, no pressure there. In the world, huh? I wanted to punch him when I saw him, but I wanted to pinch myself to ensure it happened. It felt like a fairy tale, and I'm not a princess."

Charlotte interrupts, "Only an heiress."

I smile and respond, "Charlie may not be the most eligible bachelor, but he is the best bad boy I've ever seen."

Charlotte points her finger at me, "Stay away from bad boys."

"Isn't that what we attract, Charlotte?" My sarcasm is duly noted as she smirks at me.

A woman at a table in front of us holds her cell phone to take a photo, so I smile. I missed something Charlotte said but answered, "Roland and I made no promises, although we spoke of a future. I don't think I can handle his fandom, all the comments I've read that he told me not to are from devout fans believing themselves destined to be his wife. There is an especially hopeful one, forevermrshughes. It is enough to make my skin crawl if you pay attention to her comments. Not to mention he is always gone—always traveling."

My cell phone rings; I look down to see Roland is calling, but I decline the call. My phone immediately alerts me to a text.

Roland
Halsey heiress? And you were worried about my celebrity status.

Me
Most eligible bachelor in the world?
Guess we have more to talk about.

Roland
Guess so.

Me
LOL. TTYL

"Oh, you can't be chased off by that after your history together. You knew and loved him before, and you're always traveling," Charlotte tells me. "Is he texting you right now?"

I lay my phone down and smile. Do I dare hope this could work and turn out happy? "We talk or text daily, but when would we ever see each other? We have history, but it doesn't matter. Time will tell. I'm more interested in knowing what and who my hater is."

"Try not to end this relationship before it even has a chance, please," Charlotte chides.

I have believed myself unlovable my entire life, so I have driven myself to a state of unrest. If I keep busy, I may make myself completely invisible and alone. "I'll do my best, Charlotte, but I need to be cautious. Whether he sent the letter or not, he did break my heart once." I change the subject. "Olivia, today was your first day. What do you think so far?"

"Wow. It seems like a lot has happened that doesn't normally happen on the first day, so I will hold my opinion until I have more to base it on." She holds up her glass to Charlotte and me. "Here is to an exciting and profitable future," Olivia toasts.

"Cheers," I toast. "Olivia, where are you from in England?"

She laughs, "Can't hide the accent, can I? I moved to London when I was fifteen. I stayed there through school and university. Then I moved to the US four years ago."

"Well, Charlotte and I welcome you to our small but mighty sisterhood," I say.

The driver drops me off at my apartment building hours later. While making my way to the elevator, slowly trying to hide that I am inebriated, Sam, the concierge, calls out to me, "Ms. Frost, an envelope was dropped off for you." I remove my shoes, place them and the envelope inside my bag, and take the elevator to the eighty-seventh floor.

Chapter 5

Family Portrait

I stand in the shower longer than usual this evening, letting the pulsating hot water relax my body. I slip on my old comfy pajamas that feel like an old friend considering I wore them every day while writing my novel. After pulling a water bottle out of the fridge, I take my bad habit of "Cherries Garcia" ice cream from the freezer. Armed with my treasure of treats and comfort, I pause in front of the floor-to-ceiling windows looking out over Central Park, and tonight, like every other, I give thanks for my life, even the bad times that led me here. Gathering my legs under me on the big white comfortable sectional, I take a bite and attempt to watch a replay of my interview this morning. I reach for my clipboard of loose-leaf paper, tossing my shoes out of the bag and onto the floor, knocking the envelope out. Leaning over and nearly falling forward off the couch, I reach the cardboard postal mailer and rip open the serrated edge. My cell phone rings and seeing the caller ID, Sylvia Richardson, I roll my neck from left to right, then back again. Oh shit, I forgot to give her a heads up.

"Hello, Mom."

"Dahlia?" Mom's voice is panicked.

"What's wrong?"

"There is plenty wrong besides being in a hotel. Where should I begin? Oh, I know. Were you going to tell me?" Her panicked voice has now changed to sarcastic.

"I'm sorry. I planned to call you this evening, but why do I get the impression I am too late?"

"Probably because you've been too busy being a celebrity to recall, I permitted you to use my stories only if published under a pen name. The least you could've done is give me a heads up that your real name was released before you went on national television." Sylvia's voice does not hide her agitation with me.

"I don't know what has happened on your end of this call, Mom, but it's not like we've spoken more than a couple hours total in the last six years, so why do you think I should've called you? What's happened?"

"Why should you have called me?" Mom sighs. "You've compromised me, Dahlia, and all hell has broken loose here. How could you be so careless? Bob has lost his mind." I take a deep breath and exhale. Frankly, I couldn't give two shits what has happened with my stepfather, Bob, but my mother is distraught, so I will do as I have always done and listen.

"Let's not break from tradition and have a normal talk. I'm all ears." Sylvia and I don't talk often, and it is stilted and forced when we do.

"This is important information you need to hear or believe me; I wouldn't call and bother you," Mom says. I ignore the sarcasm only slightly masked by her shaky voice. "I wasn't aware or prepared for Bob to know about your novel. I have done a great job keeping that knowledge away from him. The fact he doesn't read as a hobby has been helpful. However, things have changed after your new celebrity status and my failure to know about it ahead of time." Mom stops talking abruptly, and I hear her blow her nose. She has been crying.

She continues, "Imagine my surprise this morning when Bob yelled my name from the living room. I ran to him, thinking he had a heart attack, only to see him standing up and pointing to the television with a fire-engine-red face. There you are on GMA. I'm unsure of everything said or heard because he picked up the television and threw it. Next, he slammed the door on his way out, and I heard rocks flying as he peeled out of the driveway. He came through the front door only a few hours later, screaming at me to get out. He told me he went and bought your book and skimmed through it. Now, you know that is a lot for a man who doesn't even go to the refrigerator and get his own food. The language coming out of that man's mouth was horrible, and your name was attached at the end of each sentence."

Mom is crying now, and I don't know what to say or how to comfort her. Sylvia and I have never been good at the mother and daughter relationship. "Mom, take your time and tell me what you need to. But tell me this first, okay? Are you safe? Did he hit you? Did he hurt you in any way?"

"No. I am unharmed, and I am safe. Give me a few minutes, and I will call you back."

The call disconnects. Mindlessly, I wander into the master closet and pull down my suitcases, laying them open in preparation for being packed. I don't want to go, but I know this is what it is all leading up to. I owe her this much. She won't ask, but it's expected of me, and I guess it's only fitting. Then, I run back to the sectional to grab my ringing cell phone. "Hello. Are you better?"

"Yes, I'm sorry. Let me get this out, and I'll be fine. He was screaming at me to get out and go live with you. He said I should've told him everything before he married me. I didn't understand what he was talking about. I told him that he knew everything he needed to know. That is when he opened his copy of your book and read me a passage where you wrote about his abuse of you."

"Okay. So that couldn't have been a surprise. He did know about Dahmon and my kidnapping, right, Mom?"

"Yes, of course, but you know him. He is a narcissist, and everyone but him is wrong. He is furious with you and attempted to take it out on me again, but I didn't allow it this time. I told him I couldn't help that you chose to tell your truth in a novel and publish it."

"What did he say to that?" I ask in a calm, monotone voice.

"He said he should've never let my bratty daughter or me in his life. He said he raised you like his own and screamed that you always thought you were better than him and me and that I didn't do anything about it. He said you ruined his life and mine." Sylvia spoke at an increased volume as the story went on. I can hear the fear in her voice. I can picture the whole scenario as she tells me the story. Bob screams and pounds on the table, and Mom stays silent, waiting for the big explosion. I'm positive she's waiting for my outburst. She's not going to get it. I left that drama behind me years ago.

"What he said next is the most important, 'Dahlia once told me she would dance on my grave, but she'll see who dances on who's grave.' He said you might die first! A cold shiver ran down my spine when he said that to me, Dahlia, and now repeating it to you. I was pulling my suitcases out of the house by that time. I stopped, turned around, and reminded him, 'Over your dead body and threatening Dahlia isn't advisable.'"

"That is a threat." It is sweet justice to think of Bob threatened by none other than Mom. I feel bad for not calling Mom. I should have, but frankly, I didn't think of it. She is having trouble because I published *Daddy Issues*, and I don't know how I thought I could tell my story and still protect Sylvia.

Sylvia's voice is screeching, "He said you might die first, and

69

you'd see who danced on who's grave. I don't care how he took what I said. When did you tell him that you would dance on his grave?" I hear Sylvia take a deep breath and lower her tone. "I'm more concerned about this than you are; it is your life he is threatening." Sylvia continues, "He punched a hole in the wall as he quoted what you wrote about his advances toward you and physical abuse. He grabbed me and told me he would see you dead, Dahlia."

"He's not going to hurt you or me, Mom; I promise you." I am relatively calm because I have dealt with this kind of abuse and dysfunction my entire life. He doesn't scare me anymore. I put a stop to that years ago.

"Not me, Dahlia," Sylvia emphasizes.

"Well, I'm not worried about Bob, Mom, but thank you for telling me. He's been threatening my life since I was a teenager, and he knows what I am capable of."

"I don't think you should be so dismissive. There will be a price for the truth, Dahlia. There always is. Just ask me; I know."

"I will be there as soon as possible," I tell her.

"No, I don't want you in the state of California." Mom pleads me not to come.

"Where are you staying?" I ask her as I calmly reach over and pull an invitation-sized card out of the postal mailer. I open it while listening to Mom tell me where she is staying and why I should be scared and not come there. The blank RSVP-size card has an all-in-capital-letter typewritten message: YOU HAVE ISSUES DAHLIA FROST AND NOT JUST DADDY ISSUES. I turn the card over, unsure what I expected to see, a signature maybe. I don't know. Who sends someone a note telling them they have issues? Someone with issues. I notice the postal mailer has no postage and no return address. I'm sure this is Bob, but how did he get someone to bring it to my apartment?

"I will see you soon." I don't want to go to California. I don't want to help with this mess. But I know I am responsible, kind of. "Mom, it is probably for the best this happened now, to tell you the truth. Bob may have read the novel and knows I wrote it, but did he throw the television before or after my inheritance was discussed? You never told him, right? It won't be long before everyone knows about the inheritance. You should be out of sight just in case. I've had paparazzi show up and take photos, and you're the one who once was married to Dahmon Halsey."

"Oh, Dahlia, what have you done? I told you there is always a cost for the truth. I hope I don't have to pay for it again."

I hear her words and read the threatening card I just received. I have paid for several of Sylvia's truths and choose to deflect. "Yes, I am sorry. I should've told you sooner, but I didn't willingly divulge my identity; it was discovered, and I decided to get ahead of it."

"I'm fine where I am, Dahlia. I'll start contacting real estate agents, keeping my head down and eyes open."

"Sounds great. Are you comfortable staying in the hotel, and do you have money?"

"Yes, I am fine, and I've been using the money you sent me three years ago. This has been coming for years. I'm not broken-hearted, but it is a thirty-year marriage that's over. I'm worried about what he will try to do to you. I want to live on my own."

"If that is what you want, we can make that happen. But you are always welcome to come and live with me in New York; I have a beautiful penthouse apartment."

"No, absolutely not. I will stay in our hometown in a house I can call my own."

"We will make that happen, Mom. Don't contact Bob. Don't answer if he contacts you either, please. Good night, Mom." I give pause for only a second and think about Bob's threat. Bob and I have had blowups before, but the chances of it just going away this time doesn't seem realistic since Sylvia has left. I look down at the note in my hand and place it back in my bag. I will call the police in the morning before my appointments.

I hear the familiar notification of a message while getting ready for bed. Worried it might be Mom, I rush to see who it is.

Roland
Are you awake, love?

I rush to wash the lotion off my hands, climb into the middle of my bed, sit cross-legged, hold my phone anxiously and text back with a racing heart.

Me
Yes, I'm sorry. I forgot to text you back.

Roland
No worries. I'm leaving for LA in a few hours.
I'm hoping to see you while I'm in the States. Fancy that?

Me
Yes. I'll be in CA in a few days, too.

Roland
Brilliant. We'll talk soon, love.

I hang on to my phone, hoping he'll text again. I am shocked by the emotions this man stirs up. The last time I felt this way, I had just arrived in England and met Roland. I lay my phone on the nightstand, pull the covers over me, and twist and turn as sleep escapes me.

Chapter 6

Nightmare

January 25th

The airplane lifts off the runway, and before the wheels are tucked back into their compartment, I lay my head against the seat, close my eyes, and pray. I pray for the pilot to fly and land this plane safely and for God's hand to be involved in what transpires between me, Sylvia, and Bob. If history has taught me anything, I know a volatile situation is about to erupt. God, I promise I'll do my very best.

I open my copy of *The New York Times* and check the best seller list; *Daddy Issues* is number one. Then I saw the article with my face and the interview I gave about the Halsey inheritance. I close it. I don't know if I should've kept my mouth shut. If I had, I wouldn't be on a plane headed to rescue Mom. If I hadn't, then speculation and rumor would taint my novel. Nope, I did the right thing. I should've given Mom a head's up instead of putting her at risk.

Taking out my laptop, I list everything Sylvia needs to do, what she needs for her new house, and what I need to accomplish in the shortest amount of time to get in and get out. Home, my past life, offers warmth and oceans but reminds me of pain and dysfunction. I don't want to be here, no matter the temperature. Bob has controlled Mom their entire marriage, but she let him, which is something I don't understand and never will. He may be angry over the secrets I revealed in my novel, but he has no idea how angry I am, and he should count himself lucky I didn't tell much more. I contemplate what the path of least resistance looks like to get Mom settled and keep my distance from Bob.

Before boarding the plane, Charlotte, Olivia, and I discussed what my going home could mean for PR. Olivia's words echo in my ears. "If the person you described in your novel is angry and escalating this into something big, it could turn into a bad PR move," Olivia advises.

"It could be worse than a bad PR move, Olivia. The man has threatened my life. I plan to get in and out of the area without Bob knowing I am there or seeing his face." I mean, that is the plan—in and out.

Bob loves Sylvia in his damaged way. They have been feeding off of each other for years. I'm reminded each time I eat beef stew of the time I said something during dinner to upset Bob; I think my words were 'the roast is tough,' and he flipped the table over while I took a bite of my roast beef and potatoes. Mom cleaned the mess, set the table again, and the two of them sat in quiet and ate. From then on, she carried his food to him every meal on a tray, and he tolerated her secrecies, the things never talked about. I know she has them. He knows she has them, but no one discussed them, especially not Mom. She created her own imaginary prison walls.

I can't believe all the truth dropped in my lap since my name and novel were paired. Roland found me, and we've only touched on issues we need to discuss if a relationship could ever have a chance. Bob found out about the book after Mom successfully hid its existence for a year. The difference between the men who found out about the book is that I was more hurt over Roland than angry, and he quickly broke through my defenses, but Bob and I have bad blood and anger, and he wants to win, so do I. I gave up before and walked away from my mother to have peace. This time, she has reached out to me. I won't be walking away and leaving her somewhere she doesn't want to be—like she did to me. As a child, Sylvia taught me that showing weakness or losing control made me visible. It didn't take me long to figure out what Sylvia meant. At fifteen, Bob realized I wasn't invisible when he punched my face for the first time, lifting my feet into the air and sending me up against the truck I was standing near. When I dared to get back up, not letting him win, he knocked me down again and again. My mother told the doctors I accidentally misstepped off the front porch, smacking the ground with my face. After that, I learned to fade into the walls and not breathe loud enough to be heard, but apparently, I wasn't invisible enough when he attempted to molest me months later. So, I learned to stay invisible, strike from a distance, and not cry. Sylvia's words echo in my ears, "Quit pissing at the eyes, Dahlia."

I look around the airplane and notice the father, mother, and young man sitting to my left. They appear happy and healthy, but God only knows what goes on behind closed doors, just like all the stories my readers told me at my book signings. I know I am not the only person who suffered abuse, but maybe if there were more people to speak up about it, it would stop. It's easier to blame the victim and their subsequent behavior than the abuser who taught them those defense mechanisms. The content of my novel addresses these very issues. I take a drink of my soda and try to get out of my head, but it is impossible. This flight has to be the longest in history. Again, my mind drifts to the past. I suffered at the hands of the men with rank and power above me, just like the women in the #MeToo movement. I used to think Bob's comments when I was a teenager were abnormal, but the older I became, the more I realized how common it was for both men and women who were physically or sexually harassed or assaulted. It hasn't stopped, and no one is foolish enough to believe it has, but people are more aware. I have absolutely no guilt in speaking my truth, and if Bob has a problem with it, then Bob is the problem.

I catch myself rolling my fingers against the laptop when the woman seated to my left glares at me. With my AirPods in, I can't hear the rhythm it creates. I stop. It's not my safety and future I worry about. I got out, and I got help. Am I healed completely? Hell no. I doubt that is possible, but it's women like my mother I worry about. That is why I started the charity organization. I should've never left Mom behind, but some people don't want help. Some people won't accept help, and others can't be saved. I learned that in the military while troops tried to evacuate civilians from their homes in the middle of war zones.

Attempting again to shut my mind down, I listen to the hum of the engines and close my eyes. I tried to use some of those relaxation techniques from long ago that the therapist taught me, but it didn't work then, and it doesn't work now. Some people are a bit higher strung than others. I'm some people. There are too many memories of my screwed-up youth, not only because of parental stupidity. The memories include my own bad decisions. Memories are a tricky thing for me. As a young child, I had none. After the hypnosis, I had nightmares and flashbacks. When Mom finally gave up some truth, and I learned what happened to me and wrote the novel, I've had relief from my monsters. Still, I have flashbacks occasionally, but knowing my story and telling it helps.

Unbuckling my seatbelt, I go to the lavatory to remove myself from my thoughts until the captain tells us the temperature in Los Angeles, and we are about twenty minutes out. I take a deep breath and return to my seat.

Landing at LAX, I rent a car and drive to Santa Barbara. Driving is how I clear my head. How will Mom react to seeing me after six years? How will I respond to her? She and I have an unusual relationship; how could it be any other way than it is? If only for a few minutes, I put my thoughts on hold and turn up the music. Music is the other way I learned to cope. I roll down the window as I drive the Pacific Coast Highway. I usually bounce my words and ideas off Charlotte, but she has the entire business in her lap with me away from the publishing house. I turn the music up louder and let my mind go wherever it needs to. I practice conversations with Mom in my head while talking aloud as I attempt to drown out my thoughts.

Dread. Yes, dread is what I feel as I pull into the hotel's parking lot where Mom is staying. None of the voices popping into my head have any remarkably intelligent answers to all the questions rolling around in there. I flop down on the bed and lay back, letting my feet dangle off the side. Mom and I have had conversations, but they were short, sweet, and to the point until this last one. We've not spoken about the novel. I feel a knot in my stomach, knowing I can't put this off anymore. I work up the courage, swallow my bitterness, and begin the long walk down the hall to Sylvia's room. I stand outside the door for an extended time before knocking. Not every mother and daughter relationship can be this hard.

"I'm so happy to see you." Sylvia pulls me to her and hugs me. "Let me look at you. It's been so long since we've seen each other. You look beautiful as usual, but you're too thin." She turns and walks toward the table and chairs to sit down. She has a slight limp due to one leg being shorter than the other, which she attributes to her back surgeries. She has let her auburn hair turn gray, which is the most shocking change in her appearance.

I follow closely behind her, scolding myself for staying gone so long.

"Thank you. I'm not too thin. I am healthy now that I don't swallow my fears and anxiety. I swallow whiskey instead." I am only slightly joking as I smile. The underlying message is my attempt to draw a line in the sand. I don't want to hear her opinion on how I chose to fix the damage inside of me that she helped break. I change the subject. "You look like you've lost weight too."

"I have—about two hundred and fifty pounds of husband weight," she responds. Hearing Mom's voice and being near her, I realize I have missed her. She looks good other than shorter than before, and her shaking has worsened. I call and order a salad and a Diet Dr. Pepper from room service before contacting the bar to request three small travel-size whiskeys sent up with my dinner. I notice a copy of *Daddy Issues* with a bookmark lying on the nightstand. Her suitcases are lying open, still packed with her clothing. Her toiletries are set out neatly by the sink. I spot her "Oil of Olay" and have immediate flashbacks of watching her wash the makeup off her face as she tells me, "For every night you sleep in makeup, it ages you seven days." Thanks to her, I've never slept in my makeup. She's always been beautiful and still is. I only hope my skin looks as good as hers when I am her age.

"Mom, do you want anything?" She shakes her head no. "I've eaten already."

"That will be all. Thank you." I kick off my shoes and sit down at the table. "I knew I should've gotten you out of there, but I didn't think you would leave like every other time in the last thirty years. Are you ready to leave and not return to him in a month? We've done this a couple of times, and this is the last time I will help."

"Help? This time, Dahlia, I hate to tell you it is because you wrote your book of truths and revealed your identity. My leaving Bob hasn't always been over you, but it's been the main reason."

"I remember, believe me."

"Do you? I read the novel when you first mailed me my signed copy. Thank you for that, at least. I had to hide it from Bob, so I could only read it when he wasn't around." Sylvia picks up the book and holds it up for me to see. "I decided to reread it and remind myself what you wrote that infuriated Bob so much, and I will tell you this—it is the truth. You didn't deviate, and if your real identity were never leaked, he'd have never known the book told his secrets. On the other hand, I had to read your true feelings about me. You didn't show me in a favorable light, but I accept what I did wrong. But, Dahlia, did you have to portray me as a pill-popping mother?" She leaves the conversation to go to the bathroom. I think she would have jumped up and stormed out if she could move faster. I'm sure she'll hide in there for a bit, so I nose around the room. I remove the cap to her "Oil of Olay" and smell it. Fond memories instantly surround me. Her jewelry box sits beside her face cream, so I pick up an earring and hold it up to my earlobe like I did when I was young. I don't think I've ever seen her without lipstick or earrings.

She slowly opens the bathroom door and then sits back down, "To answer your question, Dahlia, yes, I'm ready to leave him permanently." Her look is of pain and anger, and I decide to drop it, but she adds, "You aren't quite as all-knowing and perfect as you think, Dahlia. I remember a few men you left and returned to in your days. The difference is you had the means to provide for yourself."

Standing near her, I take a deep breath before saying, "I know this talk needs to happen, but if it's all the same to you, I'd like to have it after eating and sleeping. I am here for a week, and there is much to be said between us. I want to get you settled in a house and get the movers to get your belongings first if you don't mind. I don't want you to piss me off on the first night, okay?" She is not the only fiery redhead.

"First of all, watch it. I'm still your mother. Second, there won't be any movers going to the house to get my stuff because he won't let them in, and it would be a scene. I don't care about anything except my personal items and your baby items. I'll have to get that by myself once I have a place to take it. I'll buy myself new furnishings to fill it."

"I'll furnish it, Mom."

"That won't be necessary—I saved the money you sent me. I will say this one last thing tonight about this mess. I gave you a lot of power when I told you it was okay to tell my story, but you have compromised me. I don't want you to clear your conscience by sending me money," Mom says.

"What the hell are you talking about, clearing my conscience?" I ask her as I step into the bathroom. Walk away, Dahlia. Just walk away.

"I appreciate you told me about your inheritance. The Halsey's had money, but money can't replace the years you lost and everything you had to relearn because their son kidnapped and nearly killed you, not to mention the things he did to me. I never ask you for a dime, and I don't want it. You and I need to talk about it and deal with it."

"I'm shocked at how willing you've become to talk about it and deal with it," I say as I use air quotations. "I had to beg you to talk to me. I had to beg you for years to tell me what was missing from my memories and why. Maybe with a little honesty, I wouldn't have had to undergo hypnosis to discover you had secrets." I stare at her, willingly standing my ground, but she seems fragile. I take a breath and change my tone, "I don't have anything to feel guilty over or conscience to clear. What are you talking about?"

"I meant for leaving me in California and moving away," she speaks quietly when the truth is thrown back in her direction.

"Oh. I've thought about that, Mom. You could've left but didn't. That is on you and only you. The money I have given you is from my work. I promise I will take care of you, not from my inheritance." The food and whiskey arrive just as my stomach growls, and my voice nearly matches my stomach's noise level. Although it seldom happens, we agree that it is always lovely when we can just act like normal mothers and daughters. Many things have happened over the last six years, but the relationship suffers because we've never been able to be alone and talk about what happened while I grew up. Bob never allowed Mom to go anywhere without him, and I refuse to be around Bob. My phone rings, and it is Roland. "Mom, I need to take this call." I answer, "Hello. Hang on a minute, please." I turn to Mom, "I will be back; I'm going to my room to take this call."

Opening the door to leave, Mom says, "Okay, but please come back." I hear the concern in her voice that I won't return, and I see her vulnerability. This is the mother I remember.

"I promise I'll be right back. I just need to take this call." Leaving Mom's room, I walk to my own. "Hello, Roland. How was your flight?"

"It was long. What time is it anyway?"

I look down at my watch, "It is 8:00 p.m."

"I just wanted to call and tell you I'm here, which means we are only hours apart. I can't wait to see you. But I will be here for weeks, so don't rush your visit. I have to go to New York at the beginning of March, so if something happens and it doesn't work out to see each other here in California, I will see you before I leave the States. I hope to see you in a week or so. Right?"

'Yes, I am looking forward to it."

"Are you? That is a good sign." Roland yawns.

"Yes, it is. I need to get back to my mom. Goodnight, and I will see you soon."

"Goodnight, love."

I change into pajamas, wash the makeup off my face, and stare at the horrible daughter looking back at me. No, I'm not. I had to survive.

Now, back in Mom's room by 8:20, we are both relaxed as she describes what happened yesterday right before Bob threw the TV across the room. "So, I'm sorry, but I didn't see your interview," Mom says.

"Sounds like a poor excuse for missing it," I tease, and she grins. We change the subject often as we catch up and talk about everything except what we need to face tomorrow. I show her photos of my apartment and the life I've created for myself, pictures of the inside of the publishing company Charlotte and I bought, and my penthouse apartment. She doesn't let on if she is impressed by any of it. I point to the photos of my apartment; the all-over white living room with touches of red accents, the winding staircase leading to the second floor, and photos of each of the five bedrooms and five bathrooms. I ask, "Do you like it, Mom?"

"Is everything marble and white?" Her response lets me know that she does not.

"Yes. What do you have against marble and white?"

"Nothing, but it looks like a museum. How big is that apartment?"

"Six thousand square feet. Look at all the windows, Mom. My master bedroom has the most amazing sunset view over the

Hudson River. You could have this bedroom." I tell her as I point to a photo. "You would love it."

"No, Dahlia. You love it. I would hate it. Not a chance I'm living anywhere eighty-seven floors in the air. I couldn't walk outside and feel the grass between my toes."

I stop showing her photos and put my phone away. "Yes, I love it. New York isn't for everyone."

Mom, as I expected, brings up what interests her. "I'd love to see a picture of a grandchild someday, Dahlia, but I know that's not going to happen."

"So why comment, Mom?"

"Dahlia, I love that you are happy with your life. I know you were unhappy for a very long time. Is it the money that makes you happy?"

"No. The money makes life more enjoyable, but the happiness came when I found what I needed to be content. I need peace in my life. That is something I never had until I moved to New York. I was happy living in my first little apartment in New York. I was poor but happy."

"I hope someday you know the happiness and contentment of being a mother. That is all I am saying."

"Mom, were you happy and content being a mother? Don't lie. Just think on that one, and we'll talk more about it after we get you settled. Okay? I'll let you ask and say anything you want but prepare for my answers. Moving on to the next subject." I will not discuss my lack of desire for a child with Mom. "It's getting late, and I want to know your plan for tomorrow now that I am here. Please tell me you have not spoken to Bob. He doesn't know where you are, does he? I mean, you haven't called him, right?"

"No, I haven't called him, and I'm not going to."

"Good because he doesn't need to know where you are. He doesn't need to know where I am. I gave a lot of thought to his threats, but I believe they are empty; still, we will need to stay on the side of caution."

"Yes, that is what I said. Don't dismiss his threat, Dahlia."

"Or any threat for that matter. I received a note the night you called me. It read, I have issues and not just daddy issues. It concerns me that someone tried to scare me with it. I did take it to the NYPD before I came here."

"That is scary."

"It wasn't a threat, so I can't say it scared me. It's just creepy. We need to get you settled so I can leave the state of California before Bob knows I was ever here and so I can get back and handle my own life. I think Bob will try to sue me, and that is how he'll fight back against the book, but I have your testimony, the emergency room reports to back me up, and journals I kept."

"He doesn't know about your inheritance unless he heard it yesterday. And I know he was throwing the TV when it aired."

"You still only have one TV?'

"Yes, I couldn't be in a different room watching something without him. I needed to be sitting in my chair beside him. You know what else always bothered me?" I'm not sure if she is waiting for me to answer or if she just dropped the question and left it. She finally finishes it, "I never had a dishwasher."

I hug and kiss her goodnight. "I love you, Mom. I'm going to my room, and I'm going to get a good night's sleep. We have a lot to do."

"Good night, Dahlia. I love you too, and thank you for coming to help me."

I return to my hotel room for a second time and climb into bed with a book to read. Instead, my mind has a different idea of what the word "relax" means as the last two weeks replays in my head. I question whether I believe my own bullshit. I am scared. I never intended for my name to be associated with the novel. I never expected this fallout. Roland's grand entrance into my life didn't help. I flip over on my side, turn off the lamp, and pull the covers up. Sleep eludes me as I remember why I hate coming home.

I wake ready to get this first day over with and however many more I need to get through so I can get Mom settled and get out of town. I dress and leave the hotel in a jog. The memories chase me, and I run as fast I can for as long as I can until I return exhausted. After a shower, I meet Mom for breakfast. "Let's get this show on the road. No time like the present to go out house hunting. Have you given any thought to where you'd like to live?"

"Not really. As long as it is somewhere I can have my animals and plants, and it's mine, I'll be fine."

"And two televisions and a dishwasher," I remind her.

"Yes," she smiles.

"That's doable, Mom."

* * *

We spend the day driving around and looking at properties. We spend our evening pretending to be a normal mother and daughter duo but avoid emotional topics as we agreed until she is settled into a house. On the third day, Mom chooses an older home with a fair amount of land overlooking a lake, not in the same town as Bob, and move-in ready. Later that night, with a new home to call her own, she mentions getting her belongings. "I don't like the idea of you going alone. Please ask him to leave for the afternoon. Or better yet, tell him you'll bring the law with you if need be," I suggest.

"You're not going?"

"Do you want me to go? You didn't even want me to come to California."

"No. Yes. Maybe. Just be close by."

I agree if Bob agrees to leave for the afternoon. She says, "Bob, we've been married thirty years. Tell me what you think is yours and what is mine."

I whisper, "Please, don't. It's not worth it. I went through this only a few years ago if you remember."

"Forget it, Bob. I want my stuff and Dahlia's baby stuff—things like that." Mom hangs up the phone and tells me, "Bob said he knows you're in town, and neither of us is welcome, but he'll leave for one hour, but you cannot be on his property."

"How do you think he knows I'm in town, Mom? It's not like you and I have been close. There was no way he could have known I'd come if you called."

"I don't know, Dahlia."

The following morning, neither Mom nor I are very talkative. I know I am concerned with how this day will play out. If she is concerned, she doesn't express it. Her only request is that I stand across the street at the park and wait for her. My well-thought-out plan was working until the last few minutes. From what I can see, Mom's car is completely loaded. If Bob wasn't watching and waiting for just the right second, then it is quite the coincidence that he pulls in precisely at that time. Standing across the street, I watch and wait like a cat preparing to jump. Bob taught me that much. Pacing back and forth, imagining the worst-case scenarios, I watch Bob enter the house while Mom is still inside. I shake my head, stop, watch for what I'm unsure of, then resume pacing, my steps quickening. I am unsure what he will do, and I am relieved when Mom carries out the last small box. I feel for her as I watch her try to squeeze one more memory into the only opening left in the car's back seat. All she has to show for her life fits in a couple of boxes of memories shoved into a car. Bob limps out behind Mom, following her to the car. She closes the car door, then he grabs her and turns her toward him. Anyone's guess is whether it is an accident or intentional because once I see Mom fall, I sprint across the street like an athlete at the Olympics. Bob reaches the safety of his front door before I get to her to help her into the passenger seat.

"I didn't do that on purpose. Sylvia knows that." Bob yells toward me. I'm not sure whom he is trying to assure, but I watch his expression change from concern for her to hatred of me. "Get off my property. Get off my property. I'll kill you," Bob screams.

As I step toward the front of the car, I know better than to say anything, planning to go around and get into the driver's seat, but I don't. I've never spoken up. I've never had my say until I wrote the novel. This may be the last opportunity to look my abuser in the face. Instead, I take a direct approach toward him and his house.

"You told lies in that piece of trash book of yours. You made me sound like a pervert. I never hurt you. You're a slut, Dahlia. No one believes your stories." I wave his words off as if they were a fly buzzing about my head as I take two giant steps closer to him. Deep down, maybe I want him to attack me, so it'll be ruled justifiable homicide when I kill him.

"Stories? Readers love stories, Bob. They believe what a story tells them—werewolves, vampires, witches, time travel. You don't give my readers enough credit. They know the truth from a lie. A slut and a virgin? Highly unlikely. An abusive step-father? Common. You say you never hurt me. Have you lost your mind? You hurt me every chance you could. You got off on intimidating a young girl. You are so insecure and jealous of your wife having anyone but you." My voice is surprisingly calm, but there is no hiding the hatred within it. I purposely hold myself still, other than the one hand that moves and points as fast as I think and speak. "I moved out at sixteen, you sick bastard, just to get away from you. What did you do? You used my mother and coaxed her into calling me to get me alone under the pretense of you wanting to apologize. I agreed to go the first time to appease her, but I knew what you were up to. You couldn't pass up an opportunity to try to see what you could get away with each time the chance presented itself. Do you think you shocked me the first time you drove me out on a country road and parked? You're lucky you didn't die the first time you attempted to touch me, but I was ready for you the second time, wasn't I?" I clench my fist as the blood races through my veins and pounds in my head, echoing all the prayers made by a young girl to be loved and left alone.

"I never hurt you. You always wanted your mother to hate me, and you lied until that happened." He yells loud enough for Sylvia to hear him.

I force myself to stop at the edge of the porch; all the anger I've kept buried resurfaces from that dark place deep inside me. I don't want to explode. My legs are trembling, and my hands are shaking. "Dahlia, get in this car," Mom yells. Her voice pulls me out of my rage. I take a deep breath, holding it to prevent saying or doing anything I regret. I shove my shaking hands into the pockets of my jeans.

With a calmer, quieter voice, "I tell you what. I'm not a little girl anymore, and I'm damn sure, not scared. I know how to defend myself, but you already know that. Did you ever tell Mom the reason that you limp? We will see who dances on whose grave."

Bob backs into his house. I take steps backward toward the car when I remember he has a place full of weapons, and I have none. I reach Mom's car and sit behind the steering wheel, shaking. Mom is weeping, "Dahlia, I am so sorry."

Glaring at her, "It's too late for you to be sorry, but one day he will be."

Chapter 7

Stay

Running errands and buying a housewarming gift is the excuse I give myself and my mother as I climb behind the wheel and out of my own head. I can't say I've never been so angry but if not, today was a close second. I haven't stopped shaking. Writing my truth isn't worth all this. I repeatedly apologized to Mom for letting my emotions get out of control. I kept seeing the fear on her face while she wept.

With the windows down and music playing louder than usual, I drive around my hometown and remember the few good times I had in my young adult years. Counteracting the bad years with whatever good memories I can conjure up feels counterintuitive but may be therapeutic until I get the opportunity to deal with another man who once tried to control me. I turn off Main Street and pass the high school. As I reach the intersection, I have the right of way; I get to the center when a truck rolls through the stop sign and blocks me. I slam my foot on the brake almost as fast as I slam my palms down on the horn. Seeing someone get out of the truck, I recognize Daniel's walk before seeing his face.

"What the hell, Daniel?" I ask as he leans his head into my

driver's side window, both forearms resting on the windowsill and allowing our faces to become closer than I am comfortable with.

"I waved a couple of times, but I guess you didn't see me. Either that or you were ignoring me. Which was it? I thought I'd get your attention," Daniel asks as he smiles that bright white smile.

"I didn't see you, but you have my attention now." I keep the fact he has my attention in more ways than one to myself. He is cocky, and just like Roland, he takes up space. His outgoing personality and charming smile are deceiving. "What can I do for you?"

"Nothing. I want to see your lovely face and find out when we will talk. If you come to the house, I'll toss some steaks on the grill."

I consider it for an awkward second but decline. "Tempting, but that isn't a good idea."

"Can I buy you dinner since you don't trust my cooking?"

"I trust your cooking. What is so important you want to talk to me about, Daniel?"

"I need to talk to you, Dahlia. Can't you give me that much time?"

"Meet me at the restaurant in the Hilton on Cabrillo Boulevard. I have to eat, so I don't see any harm in us visiting while I do so. I'll explain later."

"No need, I have Instagram and Twitter. I know what's going on in your life. I'm sure you don't want photos of you and your ex-husband posted, right? I'll be there at 9:00 p.m.," Daniel says as he taps the windowsill three times and turns to leave. The difference between the only two men I have ever loved is night and day. One is my good ole' bad boy, and the other is as polished as his money can buy—an angel on the right shoulder and a devil on the left. Who's to say, which is anyone's guess,

90

but I am happy to discover that I've had more desire in the past month than I've had in six years. I watch him walk away, focusing on the worn-out circle from his Skoal can on his jeans' back pocket; I am reminded why I find that sexy.

I call, "Mom, I'm staying in the hotel room one more night. Daniel needs to talk to me."

"Why doesn't he come here? Santa Barbara isn't that far from Montecito."

"I'm aware of that, but he wants to talk. Apparently, this trip home is my reckoning."

At 8:30 p.m., Daniel arrives at my hotel room. The familiar smell of blackcurrant, Italian bergamot, and oak surrounds me as soon as I open the door. If he only knew why I bought him that cologne all those years ago. I think of Roland. I attempt to turn away from him and the door, but it is too difficult not to look him up and down. I can't help it. Somehow, my man switch has been turned back on. Damn Roland and Daniel. Every time that switches on, it ends up costing me something. He is a gorgeous man who walks confidently, drawing female attention effortlessly, no matter where he goes. If someone misses his good looks by chance, they will notice and hear him coming. He has a habit of holding his keys in his left hand, then twisting them forward around his pointer finger and catching them repeatedly. It's just something he does, and I now watch him fondly. Dressed in a pair of Levi's, cowboy boots, and a dark-blue fitted shirt that fits him well, I am instantly attracted to him. He didn't have this effect on me when I saw him last fall. His arms are too big for his shirt sleeves, and his jeans fit him nicely. Daniel is 6'1", with hazel eyes and blond hair. He is easy on the eyes but hard on the heart.

Last fall, when I asked him to come to New York to discuss a business proposition, it was easy to see that he was sober. He spent several days in the city, and we had several business meetings. I agreed to invest in Daniel's sobriety and business on two conditions: one, he remains sober, and two, he had to sign a confidentiality clause stating he could not write or discuss anything about our relationship, which he willingly did. After being assured he was sober, I invested the start-up cash in his new oceanography company. I needed his assurance and silence regarding anything to do with me or my novel. So, I bought it. He rescued me once, and I'll never be able to thank him enough. Once I felt gratitude for him, it grew to love, but love faded to friendship. I couldn't stay married out of appreciation. There once was a time he and I both had issues. I am pleased to see we've both conquered our demons. He's been working extremely hard at his company from the first-quarter reports I have received, but the actual proof is standing in front of me, entirely too close.

"I thought I said I'd meet you at the restaurant, didn't I?" I step away from the door and sit down in the chair to put my shoes on.

"You did, but I got here early and thought I'd escort you to the restaurant." Daniel sits his Mountain Dew on the table. In one swift move, he picks up the chair in front of the desk and places it directly in front of the chair I'm sitting in. He gathers my hands before saying, "I want to know what's going on." Daniel isn't the type to do anything inconspicuously. Every move is executed to his advantage. Even something as simple as sitting down has to be noticed.

I pull my hands out of his and continue putting on my heels before looking back at him. "I know what you want. I'm going to tell you the same thing I told Roland." I watch as Daniel's face tightens at the mention of Roland's name. I continued, "Daniel, you and I have had our time, and it didn't work. I was always honest and upfront about Roland and my feelings for him. Even when you and I met in England when you asked me out the first time, I told you about Roland. Never in a million years could I have imagined Roland would drop into my life again and my book signing."

"But he did. What else happened?"

"You dropped into my life here in California after we met in England, too, if you remember, and it's none of your business."

"Did you sleep with him?" Daniel asks.

"Again, none of your business, but I did not. Like I wouldn't sleep with you when you came to New York. You're lucky I spoke to you again after our divorce, let alone invested in you. Don't mistake my generosity for anything other than friendship."

"I said I was sorry for everything I did, and you said you forgave me. I'm happy you didn't write about me in your book. Did Roland apologize for the Dear Jane letter and not being there when you miscarried or fell apart? It was me who took care of you and loved you unconditionally."

"Yes, somewhat. We didn't have much time to delve into the past. Look, I'm not going to discuss Roland with you. I didn't discuss you with Roland when he wanted to know about my marriage and divorce."

"So, he knew you were married? You're thinking of giving him another chance?"

"Yes, he did, and I don't know yet. I didn't marry and divorce him. Our time together was stolen from us, and I'm trying to decide if I want to get back into it."

"If you want him, then say it."

"Do you want to have dinner or not?"

"Yes," Daniel says as we walk to the restaurant. The dining room is packed, and I am thankful I asked for a booth in the back. We discuss business while eating our medium-rare ribeyes and lobster, and I can't help but laugh as I recall Roland's reaction to my bloody steak. Daniel barely notices my dinner as he devours his. He and I discuss his sobriety over glasses of iced tea, while I wish mine were at least a Long Island iced tea. I glance up, look around the room, and see the cell phone in front of the man's face, aimed in my direction. I place my elbow on the table to hide my face.

"I know you want something, Daniel. What is it?" I enjoy his company, but I can't sit here and expect not to be approached, although I am relieved that has not happened yet. The dining room has a romantic atmosphere, with candles on the tables, soft music playing in the air, dimmed lights, and couples. This is all I need.

"Bob and I still keep in touch occasionally, Dahlia." He drops this truth bomb in my lap. My face tightens, and he holds up his hand to stop me from speaking, "I'm not his friend, and no need to remind me that I signed a confidentiality agreement. You should know I'd not betray you, but you must watch your back. He's furious about what you wrote. He's mad Sylvia knew you wrote it too. I told him I knew everything you said in the book was true. I asked him what he wanted me to do about it."

"What did he say?"

"He said, 'Kill her.'"

"What? He asked you to kill me?" I spit out my words and my tea.

"No, it wasn't like that. Bob was just mad and made a bad joke. He knows I love you and would never ask me that. Maybe he wanted me to tell you."

"Would you be willing to go to the police and tell them about the phone call?"

"And say what, my ex-father-in-law is angry over Dahlia's novel calling him a pedophile and called to vent and joked about killing her? If I believed that he was serious even for a second, I would tell the police, but he's just angry."

"You can say that exactly." I can't shake the uneasy feeling of what Daniel told me even though we changed the subject ten times. I wrote the novel, and when I closed the book, I left everything that pained me on the pages. Now, damn it, it's like a story that never ends. I want a drink, and I can't have one with Daniel around. I want to finish and get out of this restaurant.

"Goodnight, Dahlia. Don't forget that I love you, too. Roland isn't the only one." Standing at my hotel room door, Daniel pulls me into his arms and kisses me. Even though I know my heart isn't in it, I let him. Why? I ask and answer my own question; I want to ensure I feel nothing but friendship for Daniel. Roland owns my heart. I'm sure of that. "I want to stay," he says. I shake my head no and step away from him.

"I'm sorry I loved you more like a friend than a husband. I'm glad we're friends, and you've always been there for me. I will always be your friend, too. Good night, Daniel." Stepping inside, I pour myself a dram. Tomorrow I'll see the Sheriff.

Chapter 8

To Be Loved

T he police officer taking my report doesn't appear concerned or convinced a threat against me was made. "I feel better just having it on file, just in case," I tell him.

A red pickup pulls out behind me as I drive away from the police station. It doesn't take a detective to see it's the same red truck Bob pulled into his drive the other day, staying back two vehicle lengths but taking the same roads and turns for several miles. The sun is shining, and a Sunday drive sounds excellent. He can't think I'm stupid enough to lead him to Mom's new house. The red truck eventually gets bored following me, so I continue to Mom's house. Today is the day I told her I would take her shopping. It would benefit me to have some mother-daughter time and show her much-needed love. "Are you ready to go, Mom?

"I don't want you to do this."

"Mom, I have all this money, and other than the charity I founded, my apartment, and your land, I've not spent a dime of it. I use the money that I've earned. You earned every penny of the money I inherited from the Halsey's, as far as I am concerned. Frankly, neither you nor I could spend it in our life-times or my offspring, so you and I are going shopping."

"Good Lord, Dahlia, how much money did they leave you?"

"Millions." She doesn't care what the actual amount is, and truthfully what's a couple of zeros? At first, I couldn't fathom that kind of money, but at least I know she'll allow me to spend money on her if she believes it is unlimited.

"I told you I don't want any of your inheritance, but if you want to spend your hard-earned money on me, that is different. Is a new car too much?" she asks.

"Deal. And no, it isn't too much." I giggle at the same woman who didn't want me to spend a dime only moments ago, but now it is okay. "I have a driver picking us up, so get ready. I'm also stopping to talk to my general contractor too. I am building a house on the woodsy part of your property looking out over the lake. Is that fine with you?"

"It's a great idea, but there is something you should know before you do. I just discovered it while reading the deed on the land."

She has my attention. "What is it?"

"This lake is the lake Dahmon drove into and where you almost died, Dahlia."

"Really?" I peer out the window and across the lake. "That's spooky, isn't it?"

"Yes, I thought maybe you should be aware before building a home looking out over it. You might prefer oceanfront."

"I'll think about it."

"I upgraded to a smartphone. It is amazing what we can research now over the Internet. It's no wonder your identity was discovered. I discovered something else today. You and a certain actor have reunited. I'm on social media, too." She picks up her phone and flashes it back and forth to show me.

"I saw it earlier. Remember? I just didn't know you had

Facebook." I laugh at her. I hate social media. "Please be careful, and don't pay attention to all the vile comments from his fans, especially forevermrshughes. Ignore anything she posts. Roland and I aren't officially a couple. Don't believe everything you read." Mom and I have kept the conversations focused on our task, but a cloud of everything needing to be said hangs above our heads. If it only sprinkles and isn't a downpour of information, I believe she and I can save our relationship.

I share with her what happened the day a man in a very expensive suit showed up at my studio apartment in Manhattanville. "He told me about my grandparents, and I was their only surviving heir. You met Dahmon's family, right? Were they wealthy back then?"

"I didn't know his family per se. After Dahmon and I were married, he took us to Kansas City to meet them once. They were wealthy, and it didn't take much to figure out he was the black sheep. I remember taking you and going out to the pool for the day to avoid hearing him fight with his parents, and the next day we left. Dahmon was an only child, so it makes sense you were the only surviving heir. They hated me, which shocks me about you receiving the inheritance."

"Why did they hate you? Dahmon was the one who abused you and kidnapped me."

"Long story, but they blamed me for his death. I've told you that before."

"Car is here. It's time." I transfer money to Mom's account before leaving on our mother and daughter shopping spree. Hours later, our last stop was at the car dealership. I distance myself and watch Mom pick out and purchase a vehicle she wants for the first time. With the final paperwork finished, the saleswoman shakes my hand and presents her copy of *Daddy Issues* for my autograph. With Mom watching me, it's one of my proudest moments until the saleswoman slides the book over in front of my mother and asks her to autograph it. Mom looks at me with tears in her eyes and shaky hands. I nod and watch her sign her name. That is my proudest moment. Mom purchases a new car, an entirely new wardrobe, and enough shoes and purses to go with each outfit by the end of the very long day. I buy her a one-carat oval diamond mother's ring and a 9-millimeter handgun.

"I don't know why I need a gun. I don't want a gun in the house. I'll never touch it."

"The gun is for your protection. You live alone. I don't know what's going on, but I have to be honest and tell you I have received several threats, or at least what I perceive as threats, even if the police don't see it that way. One is in the form of a note sent to me telling me I have more issues than daddy issues and the others are just comments over social media, but who knows what kind of person is sitting behind the keyboard typing them. What kind of person sends a note telling someone they have issues? Someone with issues. Social media and publicity have opened up a window into our entire world, not to mention Bob isn't happy with you and hates me." I decided to keep what Daniel told me to myself. I continue, "Have you noticed Dahlia Frost doesn't have social media, but Frances Slater does? I think you'll be safer if you have it. I'll pick it up before leaving town because we have a waiting period. Your car will be delivered to you, right?"

"Yes, they said to expect it in a week or two. I'm tired and ready to go home."

"Me too."

"Dahlia."

"Yes, Mom?"

"Thank you, and I love you. If you ever want to splurge on me again, can it be a vacation for you and me?"

"Sure, I have so much free time." I know that would mean

more to her than any other gift. I watch her hands and head shake and know it's time to get her to a doctor. I find it strange how small I made my world before reconnecting with Roland and now Mom. Maybe I should have faced my actual identity years ago. We use the rest of the time I'm in town getting to know each other again. The woman I spent the last week with differs from what I have ever known. It's like I've made a new friend, and that new friend is at ease and laughing. It's been a long time since Mom, and I have had time together, and we had time alone for the first time in forever. My time spent with my mother was long overdue.

Sitting on her couch in a house she owns, I witness a woman able to be herself. She can discuss the topics she wants to discuss without guarding her words. She opens up to me, which has never happened. "This has truly been a blessing in disguise. I have wanted to leave for years. You know that. I couldn't bring myself to leave him because I did love him once, and I always hoped things would change. When you were young, even when he was awful to you, I had nowhere else to go and was terrified at the thought of doing it on my own." She stands and smooths the creases in her shirt before getting a drink from the kitchen. She sits down and continues, "Dahlia, the day you stood in the doorway, looked me in the face, and told me, 'Don't leave him for me because I am leaving and I'm not taking you with me,' I knew you were strong, much stronger than I ever was or ever could be. When Bob and I got older, I thought, why bother leaving? He's not well. One of these times when his temper explodes, I fully expect that to be his end. I've had enough anger, yelling, threats, and abuse to last me an entire lifetime. I have lived scared my entire life."

"I know that, Mom, but I was sixteen when I said that and moving into an apartment of my own and expected to take care of myself. What the hell did I know? I understand what you lived with because I lived some of it with you, but that is why I ran. I hope you understand that. I wasn't going to make the same mistakes you made." I pause, not wanting to say things that hurt her. I add, "I went out and made my own." I know that if I hadn't pressed her for the truth seven years ago, she'd have never told me about my father, the kidnapping, or what he did to her. I am unsure if she has told me everything, but she deserves whatever peace and happiness she can get.

My phone rings. I glance at it and see Daniel calling, then decline the call. "I know you're angry at me, Dahlia. We've not seen each other for six years, so that was my first clue, but then I read the novel and felt your emotions with each word spilled onto the pages. I have no right to be angry about your book, and neither does Bob. I know all the mistakes and bad choices I made as a woman, wife, and mother. I could sense the tension in your words when you wrote about your childhood, the men who hurt you, and how I hurt you. I owe you an apology for my part in all the things that caused you pain, and I will say I am sorry for Bob because he will never apologize."

"Mom, I was angry at you. The anger went away, and I'm sorry to say I was left with no feelings for you whatsoever when it did. You were my mother, so what? Then I reread all my journals and wrote the novel. It became about growing and overcoming the tragedies put before us. It's about the choices we make, plus it's about choices made by others that affect us and leave us either better for them or damaged because of them. It is what it is. It manifested itself into a story of survival and healing all by itself. The hypnosis haunted me until you told me about my kidnapping." I pause and take a drink before I continue. "Honesty can be painful, but I believe it needs to be told, and I want to tell you why I went to New York and even after forgiving you that I didn't contact you or come around," I say. She nods her head but says nothing. "I didn't leave because you finally told me the truth. I left because of the first time you called and asked me to have dinner with Bob because he wanted to patch things up." I use my hands and make invisible quotation marks in the air as I speak. "I was seventeen and believed he was truly remorseful and believed if he and I could agree, then I wouldn't have to keep my distance from you. But he wasn't. He said awful things about you that no man should say about his wife, let alone to her daughter. He told me I needed to learn from a real man. He rubbed on my legs, and I was disgusted and told him I would kill him if he ever talked to me that way again or touched me."

Mom shakes her head and says, "You told me about this after, but I wish you'd have told me when it happened." She rises from the couch slowly, but once up, she stands still before taking a step. It appears she is having trouble moving her legs.

"Do you need help, Mom?"

"No. I'll be back." She leaves the room. I question if I should tell her my truths. She dabs her eyes, wads her handful of Kleenex into her left hand, then sits back down.

"Let's not talk about this anymore. It's the past, and it's over."

"Oh, no. I need to hear this. I buried my head in the sand when you tried to tell me. I read your words in the book; somehow, seeing them written made it real. Continue, please."

"Mom, living it made it real. I'm done talking about it." I watch her for a few minutes before she replies.

"I need the truth, Dahlia."

"Okay." I pace the living room floor as I tell her, "You just said you wished I'd have told you when it happened; why? Because right before I moved to New York and before you told me the truth about the kidnapping, you called me again. I was twenty-nine years old. I'd spent five years in a downward spiral of my own and finally pulled myself out of it when you wanted me to patch it up with Bob." I shake my head. "Mom, you took a pill to get out of bed, a different color pill to function throughout the day, and several more to sleep. You didn't have a clue what was going on outside your world. He wanted to take me to dinner and out on a ride. You wanted me to patch it up with him again. I refused to go because I knew he hadn't changed. He was using your desire to have me in your life to get to me. But, you said, and I quote, 'I can see how much you love me. You won't even try to fix this.' When I hung up the phone with you that day, I knew that was it. You were willing to put my life in danger to make him happy, or so he'd leave you alone, I'm not sure which. I agreed, and I'm not sure why—to make you happy or make him pay." I pour myself another whiskey and sit back on the couch beside her.

"That time, he didn't just want to talk, and he attempted more than to molest me. I was a grown woman. He was determined to hurt me. I tried to get out of the vehicle, but he caught my hair and pulled. I slid back on the seat, and when I turned to put my feet back in, I kept up the momentum. I went prepared for him. I took the kitchen knife out of my coat and jammed it in his right leg. I left him with a choice: bleed to death or drive himself to the ER. I walked five miles back to my house that day. Didn't you ever wonder or ask how he got the injury?" My face wasn't angry because I didn't feel anger at her anymore. I'm sure my expression just begged for a reason.

She gasped, "Yes, Bob said he was cleaning fish, and the knife slipped. I am so sorry. I should have never asked you to go. I hoped the two of you would fix the conflict between you," she said while looking down at the floor. She continues speaking in a whisper, "I was raised in a different time than you, Dahlia. Parents did things to their children without police or agencies telling them they couldn't. Men did things to their wives because we were their property. When Dahmon hit me so hard that he knocked me through a wall, I called the police. The officer asked me what I did to make him angry. When he poured a pan of hot water over me while I slept because I refused to get up and cook for him and his buddies in the middle of the night, I was just grateful it wasn't boiling water. You were sleeping right beside me. I love you very much, and as long as you know that, that is all that matters."

"Is it? I am so sorry for the abuse you suffered in your life. I will tell you something, and I mean it, I will be a distant memory if you ever go back to him. I will be someone you once knew; I swear that to you. I don't know how to be a parent, but I know you failed, yet I love you unconditionally."

"Is that why you've not had children?"

Mom looks down as she asks me. It occurs to me that she also needs reassurance that my childhood isn't why I have willingly forgone having children. "Mom," I reach for her hand and hold it. "I will say this one last time, and I need you to hear me. My choice not to have a child has nothing to do with you or my messed-up childhood. Not having children has not been a conscious choice because the opportunity never showed itself after my miscarriage. When I married Daniel, I knew it was a mistake before I said yes, so the thought of a child with him never crossed my mind. He loved me and still does. I loved him or tried to, I should say. I wanted to love someone, and I needed someone or something to ground me, but the marriage wasn't the answer. As I've told you before, I only truly loved one man, and when that ended, and I miscarried our child, I made up my mind that no one else could have any part of me. I had failed at everything."

"Failed? Dahlia, we all fail at parenting and other relationships involving our hearts. The strong get back up and try again."

"I did. I married Daniel. Look how that turned out, secrets

and betrayal. I can't take any more secrets or betrayals from anyone, especially you. Mom, there aren't any more secrets, right? Anyone knowing my real identity and wanting to dig into my life isn't going to find anything I don't know, right?"

"Not that I know of." She hesitates for a minute before continuing, "I'm happy you and Roland found each other again and have chosen to reconnect. You never know what the future holds. You're still young. What is happening between you and Daniel?"

"Nothing. We're just friends. I had no idea Roland would enter my life again. I've been married to my writing and pregnant with this book. I'm sorry, but giving you a grandchild isn't part of my plans. I'm happy with my life, and you seem happy. What else can we hope for?" I don't even believe what I just said because seeing Roland has been uppermost on my mind since I left him in London.

"Dahlia, I know you are leaving tomorrow, and I've loved spending this time with you. I appreciate everything you have done for me. But learn something from me, please. Find true love, and don't run from it. You're too strong to be stuck, so I don't worry about you living my life. Don't let the past rule your future. Give up control for once and go with your heart."

My phone rings, and I glance down to see who is calling. It is Roland. I decline his call.

"Mom, I love you, too. We've accomplished a lot in a short time. Good night. I'll see you in the morning for breakfast."

Chapter 9

Malibu

February 3rd

Regret is a foreign concept, especially after leaving my mother; I usually want to run as fast as possible and not look back. This time is different. Olivia arranged a book signing in Santa Monica, which eased my conscience about leaving Mom to see Roland, but now I'm going to work. I listen to Roland's voicemail, asking if he will get to see me in California. I'm as anxious to see him as he appears to see me, but I don't know how wise it is. Slightly forgetting the distaste on my tongue for California, I enjoy its sunny, beautiful weather and the scenic drive along the coast, lost in thought and music. I am startled when a loud ringing replaces the music over the speakers.

"Hello, love," Roland's soft voice stops the loud ringing assault. "Where are you?"

I turn the volume down, "Good morning. I am on the Pacific Coast Highway headed to Santa Monica. What about you?"

"I'm at a hotel in Malibu enjoying the beautiful weather California offers."

"I'm happy to hear that. Thank you for texting me photos and making me envious of your vacation while I was at my mother's dealing with life," I tell him sarcastically.

"No problem," he jokes. "Listen, we rode motorbikes yesterday. We thought about it again today, but it's been a week, and I wondered if you were headed in this direction this morning. Since you are, does that mean I will see you today? Thought maybe you'd like to go riding with me."

"That's sweet of you. That sounds fun. I want to see you before returning to New York, but I didn't know how feasible that was with your schedule and mine. It sounds like we have today free, though. I planned to drive to my hotel, Shangri-La in Santa Monica, and then call you, but...." I pause. "Would you like to meet me there?"

"I don't want to read anything into that loaded question, love, but I'd be a fool not to. Are you asking me to come to stay with you? I want nothing more than to hold you if that answers your question." I hear the mischief in his voice. I decide to own up to how much I want to see him.

"You know what? How about I come to Malibu instead? There is no sense in me passing Malibu on my way to Santa Monica. I'll call and reserve a hotel room. Where are you staying?"

"That sounds like a great idea. I'll get you a room as soon as we get off the phone. I'm at the Malibu Beach Inn and checked in under Robert Burns. What time do you think you'll arrive? What are you driving?"

"Robert Burns, that's funny." I enter the hotel address into my maps, "I'll be there around noon, Robert. I'm driving a small, dark-blue two-door with dark tinting."

"What make?"

"I'm not sure. I didn't pay attention. Something that blends in and doesn't draw attention."

"I'll be watching for something invisible." He laughs. "See you soon."

I am excited to see him. I am hopeful for whatever these days together bring, believing we'll either rekindle something that once was wonderful or spend time like old friends. Either way, Roland will be back in my life. He makes me feel alive, and I am going to welcome it. No one else I've ever known makes me feel the way he does—no one. I've denied my feelings since seeing him in London. I've known nearly nineteen years; he is the one for me.

At noon, I pull into the hotel parking and see him standing outside the front doors. When I pull into a parking spot, I watch his palpable nature draw two women to him as he smiles, and they snap photos. It crosses my mind that either he doesn't realize he isn't just a regular guy who can hang around outside, or he loves that everyone wants to be close to him; everyone wants to love him. I glanced down, put the car in park, and by the time I shut off the ignition, the same gorgeous man had opened my car door.

"I missed you. It seems it's been months, not weeks since we saw each other." Roland takes my hand and pulls me up to him and into a hug. He smells of sun and sweat and everything the word masculine entails.

"I wouldn't leave California without seeing you," I tell him as he pulls one of my suitcases behind him with one hand and holds my hand with his other. My insides feel bouncy. I'm giddy, and this feeling is why I don't need any reminders of why I am here.

"Let's get you settled." We stop in the lobby, and the bellhop takes my bags, then he continues toward the elevators. "I need to check in."

"No need; I already took care of everything."

"Thank you," I tell him. "How's your mum?"

I start to recap only a part of the story before I realize I am talking nonstop, and it is a very long story I don't have the desire to tell right now. We're focused on each other and not paying attention to what's happening around us until we stop at the elevators. Looking around the room enables me to notice we are being watched. All eyes are on Roland and staring through me. Somehow, that comforts me. I love standing beside him because no one sees me, and I feel invisible. "Are you all right? Did you hear me?" Does he even realize his effect on others, not just women but everyone he encounters?

Roland places his left hand on the small of my back, reaching in and touching my heart, as he always seems to do. He guides us onto the elevator and stops at the third floor. When we step into the room, I see some of his items. "Is this your room, Roland?"

"Yes. The hotel has no vacancies. I'd prefer you stay here with me tonight, anyway. You know I can be a gentleman; I've proven that." The bellman arrives and brings my bags inside. "Then, I'll go to Santa Monica if you want. We can do another signing together. I want as much time as I can get with you. Is that all right with you?" he asks.

How could that not be all right with me? There is sexual tension between us heavy enough to bring the building down around us. How could I not want him? It wasn't easy when in London, but I wasn't sure I even liked him. Now, I am painfully aware that we enjoy each other and have forgiven the past. "If you're planning on being a gentleman, I think I will go on to Santa Monica."

He smirks, "What would you like to do first? This is the first day of your vacation, right? It doesn't sound so far like this past week has been even close to relaxing. Riding? Beach?"

"I'd love to spend the day at the beach. I want to enjoy the sand and sun, lying under a cabana on two loungers with too many drinks and nothing but time so we can catch up. That sounds good to me. How about you? Not about anything serious, though, okay?" He agrees. Minutes later, dressed in my new bikini I purchased just in case this situation arose, it crossed my mind to tell him I'd prefer to stay in the hotel all afternoon and ravish him, but I didn't want to appear too eager. It will benefit both of us to work for it, at least a bit. We're led to our cabana, walking out onto the beach, hiding our faces as best we can under hats. Roland's telling me quite animatedly how he's been keeping busy. He is amusing. On the other hand, I try to hide the drama and threats against me, but he senses I am leaving things out of my story.

"What else? You forget I know your family history. What else happened?"

"I don't want to cloud our day with all that."

"Don't cloud it. Just haze over it, then."

I briefly tell him about my visit with my mom and the fight with Bob. "Well, it sounds like some good came out of it if you and your mum are on speaking terms again."

Later, the more I drank, the friendlier I became, and being visible didn't seem so scary. The photo I saw on social media of him and a woman having lunch might have had something to do with my willingness to be seen. While Roland bravely takes it upon himself to search out drinks, I run into the ocean, dancing around seductively in my tiny bikini while calling out his name to join me. Roland, of course, would never leave a lady standing somewhere on her own, especially while singing Lover, Lover by Jerrod Neiman. Knowing he'd not venture too far from me, I searched his whereabouts. His head turns toward me, cupping his hand around his ear to hear my song. I watch as a smile crosses his face, and he bends slightly forward, laughing before he begins a stroll to join me in the ocean. Women with phones in hand close in on him from different directions for their photo op. He starts running toward me. I watch him in slow motion until he reaches me, but instead of slowing down, he tackles me. We let the waves carry us farther out. I wrap my arms around his neck and kiss him deeply for the world to see. Neither of us cares who is watching or taking photos. Today, he is just an ordinary man on vacation with a woman who thinks he holds the moon and stars. Several minutes later, tired from the waves hitting us, we lay back down on our loungers when Roland remembers our drinks are still empty. He wanders off somewhere, yet again, to get us a drink and be admired.

I let the sun's heat sauté my skin and bring out the aroma of margaritas marinated in ocean water. I bask in it as my body relaxes. A shadow casts shade on my body. Believing the shadow to be Roland standing over me, I say, "Would you mind rubbing me down with sunscreen?" as I hold the sunscreen up to him. I lift my sunglasses to see why not when no quick reply is given in a seductive Scottish accent. When I open my eyes, the person standing before me doesn't look familiar. I sit up and remove my sunglasses as he steps under the cabana. I grasp my legs and pull them up around my chest, a habit I have adopted young that has stayed with me to protect myself when exposed and vulnerable—lessons learned to defend me, I assume. My first reaction is to scream, but I don't want to call attention to myself. He looks like a physically fit and distinguished older man with a kind smile, but looks can be deceiving.

I don't know if this man ever did anything to me, but I can't stand him near me. What if he did? Would he have the guts to approach me? Maybe if he thought he got away with it. Perhaps he thought it was a hookup. I just don't know, and the police thought I was crazy and found no reason to press charges on someone I couldn't even say may or may not have drugged and raped me.

I hide my eyes behind the dark lenses of my sunglasses and

quickly scan the surrounding area looking for Roland. I spot him posing for photos with two drinks in his hand, one of which I wish I had in my hand to throw in Derek Duncan's face.

"Dahlia, I thought that was you," Derek says. Derek reaches down and picks me up like a child. He moves so quickly that I can't stop him. He turns his body and sits down on my lounger, placing me on his lap. I outstretch my long legs and push off his lap. Jumping off with such force that I land my dismount, I fall backward in the sand. Derek stands up and reaches down, pulling me up into his arms.

"Don't touch me." I push him, and he falls back on my lounger. Making a run for it, I trip over my feet in the sand and fall again. I crawl my way back up and into a run toward Roland, who has seen what just unfolded. I reach Roland's arms, and he wraps them around me, dropping our drinks.

"What's wrong?" Roland asks as he still moves us toward the man who frightens me. Now, what do I say? I can't tell him this ugly story as he walks toward the cabana and the man standing under its shade. "Do you know him?" I shake my head no. Then I shake my head yes.

"Maybe," I say and lift my hands in an I don't know pose.

"Let's go find out."

Roland closes the distance between him and Derek as I stand frozen. I watch as Roland's massiveness and Derek's massiveness square off. The man takes steps back, and Roland waves me over. Oh, I can't. I don't know what to do. He waves for me again. I hesitantly walk toward Roland, arms wrapped around my waist while begging my feet to move. As I approach, I hear them talking. "Yes, I think it's been eleven years," Derek says. He reaches for my hand to shake.

I step behind Roland. "Do you know this man?" he asks.

I pause for a long time before answering, "I didn't think so, that is why when he manhandled me, I freaked out, but now he looks familiar." Roland wraps his arm around my shoulders and pulls me into him.

"This is Derek Duncan. I met him years ago when I arrived in Hollywood."

"I'm sorry, Dahlia. I didn't mean to scare you. I thought you would remember me. We met eleven years ago at a premiere. "Imagine my surprise," he says as he smiles at Roland and then back at me before continuing, "I wasn't sure it was you, but when you removed your hat and turned to face my direction, I knew I'd only known one auburn-haired and brown-eyed woman that beautiful. I shouldn't have touched you. I am sorry. Do you forgive me?"

I ignore him while I move to my lounger, slightly behind where Roland is standing. As evident by his following comment, Derek isn't getting the hint that I have nothing to say to him.

"How did you end up with this guy?" He laughs. Roland smirks awkwardly.

"I didn't end up with him. I think he's perfect," I state as though protecting what Roland and I have. I don't like this guy for multiple reasons. My tone is intentional. I sit on my lounger and push my sunglasses back over my eyes.

"I'll be right back, love. Why don't you relax?" Roland says. I don't glance up as he walks with Derek to the bar until Derek speaks.

"Goodbye, Dahlia. It is nice to see you again."

I hear Roland tell him, "You shouldn't have touched her," as they walk away. I can't believe what just happened. Apparently, I have been under false assumptions for eleven years. I remember this man feeding my friend and me drinks all night, dancing, then waking up in a hotel naked and alone, not knowing what had happened. The police said the hotel room I woke up naked in was registered in my name and was paid for with cash. I didn't have money in my purse, let alone a thousand dollars.

Roland returns, sits on his lounger, and hands me a drink. "Are you okay, love? I made this one a double." He gives me a Manhattan. "That was strange. I will never forget your eyes when you reached me. You were terrified. Although, who wouldn't be? What kind of man does that?"

"Exactly. Who does that?" I take a large sip of my drink before he pulls my face to his, bends forward, and kisses me. We enjoy an hour of uneventful relaxation.

By the time we reach the hotel room, I have put the past back in the strongbox of my memories where it belongs, but I will never forget it or his face. I immediately strip off my swimsuit and step into the shower. Roland speaks with an increased volume and urgency from the bedroom, "Oh shit. I forgot we have a party to attend tonight."

"You've got to be kidding me," I yell back as the water spills down my body onto the shower floor.

"It's a cast party. Sort of a get-together to reminisce about the series and celebrate its success. We all worked together for years; we get together when we're all in town." I open my eyes as his voice becomes louder. My body reacts to his presence as I watch him strip off his clothing and step into the shower. With today's events behind us, my fear of being hurt while in Roland's protective arms is minimal. All I feel is desire, and it is nice to know I can still feel this way. I want him. My eyes stare at his nakedness as he stares back at mine. Naked and without anything to guard our hearts, I pull Roland's body to mine under the hot water. I initiate our embrace by pulling his mouth to mine. I run my hands over his wet body, grab the washcloth, lather it to get it sudsy, and wash him, paying particular attention to specific areas more than others. He pins my arms against the shower wall, kissing me. When he lets go, he turns me away from him, bending me slightly forward and sliding his hands to my hips. He leans over my body to kiss the nape of my neck. I moan loudly and brace myself as my body reacts to his presence and touch as his thrusts increase in intensity. He grabs my long hair and pulls my head up. I am more than willing to let him take my body; I welcome it, but it will take a lot more than sex, no matter how good the sex is, for me to let him into my heart again. My body aches for him, but I'm keeping my soul out of it. "Am I hurting you?"

"No, anything but," I sporadically answer, finding it hard to get my breath.

He uses his foot to spread my legs farther apart and thrust deeper inside me. He slams his body into mine, moving me forward and pulling me back to him with each thrust. Roland loves me until my body begins to spasm. I feel my body release for the first time in years as we enjoy each other until the water runs cold.

Still dripping water from the shower, he carries me to the bed and lays me down while standing over me. "I've never forgotten you, Whisky Girl; since you collided with me and touched my heart, you've owned it. You need to remember that my actions are true, not the tabloids, if this is going to work. You don't think I missed the photos of you and your ex-husband having dinner right after I had lunch with a female friend, do you? I don't know jealously, but I'm protective over the people I love." He pulls me off the bed and into his arms.

My legs are weak and trembling when I throw my arms around him and bury my face into his neck; I have forgotten what it is to give myself to a man and the emotional release from orgasm. Kissing him, I try to get closer than a physical body can. I believed those mushy love feelings were dead inside of me. Do I let him get this close, or do I run now? Is it even possible? Can

I fall back in love with him this easily, or is what I am feeling just lust?

"Try not to get me in trouble tonight," Roland says as he taps my backside before walking away.

"I didn't get us in trouble today or draw attention to us. Derek Duncan did."

"I was teasing, Whisky Girl, I'm sorry. The party is at my friend's house, my TV wife, and her husband's."

"Oh, goody. I can hardly wait."

"It will be a who's who of movie stars. You'll have a good time."

"You would think so, but I doubt it. Your co-star has seen you naked more times than me. Wouldn't that bother you if the entire world saw me naked on national TV?"

"Have you watched any of the series yet? Why do you say I'm shown naked? I'm never totally naked."

"Charlotte told me. I haven't watched it yet."

"You bring up good points. I'm going to say no, it wouldn't bother me, but I'm glad you're an author and not an actress. Just try to have fun."

The party is a casual dress affair, but I ensure to look every bit the part of a beautiful woman worthy of being with him. It is not easy for a woman to stand beside a man so admired, loved, and impeccably dressed, not to mention his own beauty, and be seen. Tonight, I want to be seen. I wear a black cocktail dress and a pair of Louboutin heels to make my already long legs look longer, and I wear my long hair down and free-flowing. My hands haven't stopped shaking since I left London, and now I have flutters in the core of my being; it has me off balance. The hair on my arms has stood up all afternoon, but I attribute that to the encounter with Derek. Seeing I am nervous about meeting the actress who played his television wife, Roland offers comfort, "You want to know a secret?"

"I guess." I am half paying attention to him as I finish getting ready and panic over meeting these movie stars. Roland is a movie star, and I'm sure one of the very best once I watch one of his movies or series. But I've known him for what feels like forever. He's not Roland, the movie star. He is Roland, my first grown-up love.

"Do you want to know one of the things I love about you that I've never told you before?"

"Of course." Now he has my complete attention.

"My love for you doesn't exist on a calendar or a clock, nor does it understand time or distance. I've existed and moved forward with my life, but as far as my heart is concerned, we haven't missed a day since we kissed goodbye at the airport."

He has my full attention and heart as I look into his eyes and peer into his soul. He continues, "I love that you are all I see when you enter a room, and I am blinded to anyone or anything else. You look amazing, love. I can't wait to introduce you. Now, hurry up and get ready."

Chapter 10

A Scary Time

Arriving at the private home of Roland's co-star and her husband in the hills of Hollywood would've been intimidating, and my self-confidence might have been shaken if it weren't for the knowledge that I alone hold Roland Hughes's attention. Welcomed into a 1960s retro-decorated room filled with fabulously famous and gorgeous people, I hold on to the man whose arms reach out for me. I know I am safe and in good hands. "Maggie, this is my Whisky Girl." Roland smiles and looks at me then back at Maggie, "Dahlia, this is Maggie." I am star-struck and extend my hand to shake Maggie's, but instead, Maggie leans in and hugs me.

"I've heard so much about you. You look lovely," she says as we look each other up and down as women genuinely do.

"Coming from you, that is a compliment."

Maggie loops her elbow around mine. I glance back at Roland before Maggie says, "Should I call you Dahlia or Frances?" As she escorts me around her home.

"You may call me either, but my name is Dahlia."

"Yes. I've seen the publicity. I watched your interview when

GMA announced you were the Halsey heiress. How surprising that must've been to discover." I sense she has something else on her mind she wants to say as she leads me upstairs and away from other ears.

"The inheritance, or that they mentioned it on GMA?" I ask.

"I mean the inheritance you knew nothing about." She continues showcasing her home, in and out of four of the five bedrooms. It is a beautiful home decorated in more color than I'd prefer. I have more of a white palate with a touch of red for color taste. She is more color, only dulled down by a touch of white. She leads me into what I assume is her and her husband's master bedroom suite and closes the door behind us. Why pick this room? Odd.

"You should've seen his face and heard his voice last year when he finally found out you wrote under a pen name; you'd have thought he just won an Academy Award. His sister-in-law read your book and told her husband, and he told Roland."

"Yes, I'm aware. Roland told me. I had no idea what he was doing or where he was; it's fortunate he found me."

"Really?" She says that as if she doesn't believe me.

"It's a long story, Maggie. I'm sure he'll fill you in someday." Now I understand her choice of rooms. She wants to have a more intimate and intrusive discussion. It doesn't bother me, but why?

"I know a little bit. He mentioned something about a Dear Jane letter."

"He told you about that?"

"Yes, Roland and I share almost everything." Her tone seems possessive and telling.

"I've been told about that, too. I'm happy Roland had a confidant in my absence." I want her to know that I know what she isn't saying. She is afraid I will break his heart. She has only heard his side of the story. She is his friend and doesn't require my side.

Walking back toward the party, she stops, then adds, "I read *Daddy Issues*. I know about the miscarriage too, and he had no idea about a child. He was crushed when he read about it."

I want to say so much, but I choose to give her the benefit of the doubt and believe she is only looking out for Roland's best interest, having his back. I smile and whisper, "I was crushed when it happened, so I know how that feels." Maggie tightens her lips and stops talking as she leads me to the great room, where I take larger steps than I should in these heels to reach Roland. I stand close to him as he drapes his arm across my shoulders, hugging me into him. Maggie stares at me, and I try to give her an assuring smile that I won't hurt him, but I can't assure her or Roland any more than I can be assured Roland won't break my heart.

My stomach growls. Roland says, "I'm hungry, too. We worked up an appetite today, didn't we?" I smile and nod. We sit outside on the balcony overlooking the Pacific Ocean while we eat. There is a beautiful breeze while the sun is setting. It would be incredibly romantic if we were alone, but I have already learned to enjoy each minute out of the public eye.

"What do you think of Maggie?" Roland sips his wine and looks over the rim of his glass at me as he asks me the question. I want to answer his question with a few of my own, but I choose to mind my own business.

"I find her lovely and an obvious fan of yours." Smiling, I bite my tongue.

Roland looks up first when my name is called. Once I turn my head toward the voice, it all happens so fast; Derek grabs my arm and, with it, a hand full of my hair and pulls me out of the chair, leaving me off-balance. Derek knocks a chair over in the process that thuds against the concrete. Roland pushes out of his chair; the iron table scratches against the concrete, the drinks spill as glass shatters, and our dinner spatters as it hits the concrete below us as he comes around to my side. The noises are deafening. Roland grabs Derek trying to pull him away from me. However, Derek doesn't release me, pulling on my arm, thereby pulling me forward with an entire hand full of hair. I try to bat Derek away from me, but a scream leaves my lips as he wrenches my hair tighter in his closed fists; stars dot my vision, and pain shoots up my legs as one of my high heels loses footing. He releases his grip as he takes a swing at Roland. My hair is now free, and I watch him fail to land his punch. I step back just as Roland swings and lands his fist on Derek's face. Watching Derek's head rocked to the side and the blood from his nose spatter is similar to watching a close-up replay of a boxing match.

I hear his words at the time of impact, "I just want to talk to...." The power behind the swing lifts Derek off his feet and crashes him onto the deck as more glass resounds through the patio, and people gasp and shout.

Now protected in Roland's arms, I see Maggie step onto the patio and stand near us, looking down on Derek. Everyone looks up and sees a flash from another guest's camera. Some people laugh, and some stare while I look down at Derek lying at our feet. Derek didn't know what hit him. "Are you all right?" Roland asks as he holds me at a distance to look at me. My scalp stings and I rub my arm. I glance at Derek lying on the ground, then back up at Roland, still unsure what just happened and astonished at how fast it happened.

"I think so," I answer as I see the long strands of my hair wadded in Derek's fist.

"What happened, Roland? Do you know who that is?" Maggie asks and looks up at her security, which has made its way to the patio. She points to Derek, "Assist him up and out of my house. He is drunk. Do you want me to call the police, Dahlia? He has assaulted you."

Roland answers for both of us. "Yes, I know who he is, the same asshole who grabbed Dahlia this afternoon on the beach and again just now, and yes, call the police so she can press charges."

I shake my head yes in confirmation. I release myself from Roland's arm and leave the patio. I want to go.

Walking away, I hear Maggie say, "Okay, Roland, but Derek Duncan is an agent and music producer here in Hollywood. Do you know him?"

"I'm sorry, Maggie. Yes, I know who he is. I bet he'll remember me after tonight as well."

Roland meets me in the foyer, shaking hands and saying goodbye to his friends and well-wishers as we prepare to wait outside for the police to arrive.

Security assists Derek out the front door, and as he passes us, he stops in front of Roland. Roland moves me into him closer. "Maggie, Dahlia, Roland, I want to apologize. I just wanted to talk to you, Dahlia," Derek says as he holds the bag of ice over his lower face.

Roland steps forward in front of me. I can speak for myself. I stretch my neck around Roland, "What the hell, Derek?" I blurt out. "I don't know who you think you are but stay away from me."

Roland stands his ground and warns him, "That isn't much of an apology. I suggest you learn better self-control. I've apologized to the other guest, but I won't apologize for hitting you, and if you touch her again, a bag of ice won't fix what I will break." We step outside and give our statements to the police as Derek is assisted into the back seat of his free ride downtown. We all know he won't stay downtown long. I know this sort of man; he is a man who believes he can have every young woman he wants because of his place of power—the kind of man who is now being arrested and losing everything because of their actions. I can't believe he escaped the highly publicized MeToo movement. Why his sudden interest? Why risk me coming forward to the press with what I think about him?

It's late when Roland and I get back to the hotel. He's in a mood to talk. I'm not sure why he thinks tonight will be a good night to discuss all the things we still need to talk about, but I disagree. I'm in no mood to hash over old wounds. Instead, I want to be close to him. It is odd after what we experienced tonight, but my mind is running wild with thoughts and desires for him. I want to punish something, and I am hoping Roland will participate. I grab his wrist and pull him close to me. He places one hand on the small of my back and the other wrapped up in my hair at the nape of my neck.

"You used to love for me to lead you. Let me lead you." He gently pulls the back of my hair, tilting my head up to meet his before I feel the hunger of his kisses possess and hold me captive. Stepping back, I remove my dress and stand before him in nothing but stilettos, black thigh highs, and lacy under-garments.

"Those are lovely, but I prefer you naked."

I smile and quickly get naked. He picks me up, lays me on the bed, then lays beside me. I roll on top of him and spread my body over the top of his. I can't calm the unsettled feeling of being touched or talked to in a way I didn't want, abused, or left feeling powerless. No, I can't let him lead me.

Roland whispers, "I love you. I want to love you all night so that you know when we are apart; I am always right here, and here, and here, and here. I will always protect you." He touches a different spot on my body. I can't let my guard down to make love to him, not yet, but I need him. I need him more than I want and more than I want him to know.

He attempts to be gentle and loving with me, kissing my lips and trailing down to my neck, whispering words of love. He suddenly stops when I tell him, "I don't want you to make love to me. I need you inside my body, not my heart and head." He pauses and looks wounded for a second before he lifts my head to stare into my face before flipping me off him and pulling me up on my knees while he is on his knees behind me.

Leaning his tall torso over mine, he whispers, "Answer this question carefully; whose arse do you love more, his or mine?"

I twist my head around, "Arse? His? Who?"

"You know who? Your favorite actor, Charlie. I saw you staring at him tonight before all hell broke loose. I was going to introduce you but decided not to."

"Oh, him." I'm laughing so hard that my words are fragmented as I speak. "Your... arse... is... only... second... to..." I can't help teasing him, and I am thankful he intentionally made me laugh to lighten the mood. Tonight was intense for both of us; he knows me well enough to know that I don't sit in pain and think about it. I pull back, lick my wounds, and move on.

"Second to who?" He slaps my ass.

I collapse on the bed in laughter. Roland lies beside me with the moment gone, laughing as I tell him, "Don't make me compare arses, babe. That's a hard one. You know I love men who ride horses, Harleys, and Audis." I grip the hand he punched Derek with and kiss it.

"Let's get up and talk about tonight. You don't have to bury these things anymore. I am here for you and always will be."

"No. There is no need." Roland's suggestion of an intimate discussion kills the laughter and squashes my need to be near him. I roll away but only for a second. I think about his willingness to talk to me, which is not something I've ever had, so I roll back immediately and test his willingness. "If you can answer this one question for me, I will tell you everything and anything you want to know about me and my lost years that you don't already know."

"Okay, I will give it a go. What?"

"Why do men want to possess me, change me, or hurt me?"

His pause extended, the look on his face was painful, and I wish I hadn't asked him. He takes a deep breath, "I don't want any of those things. I can only speak for myself. I want my Whisky Girl back, whom I have loved my entire adult life. I miss her."

"She's gone, Roland," I whisper, moving to his side, and folding into him. "If you want me, you have to love this version of me." I kiss him deeply, desperate not to push him away or run him off. He pulls me into the fold of his body, and I whisper, "Good night."

"Good night, love," he says as he plays with my hair.

I wake to the sun shining through the windows. I had to have gotten at least a couple of hours of sleep. Roland is sleeping peacefully beside me when I sneak out of bed. I take two Tylenol and make a pitcher of bloody Marys and two pieces of dry toast before stepping out onto the balcony of our suite. Lying on the lounger, only wearing Roland's t-shirt from last night, I scan my social media sites to see which photos we are tagged in. I type "Dahlia Frost" into the search bar, *"Halsey Heiress Identified, Author Frances Slater is the Halsey Heiress."* I type "Frances Slater" into the search bar and see professional photos of me alone and the cover of my novel. Then I google Roland's name. Tons of headshots and professional photos pop up.

Against my better judgment, but determined to be aware, I check Twitter and Instagram. There are photos of Roland and me on his pages and my author page. I can't help but laugh when I see a picture of Roland tackling me in the ocean, nothing but ass and elbows. There are photos of us at the London book signing. While we were in London, Roland told me that if I wanted to be with him again, I would have to get used to the media attention he evokes. It seems the attention I arouse on my own has heightened. I continue to scroll and see a photo of Roland and me after he knocked Derek to our feet. Other than the apparent invasion of privacy these photos evoke in me, I take it in stride. I accept that I will have to get used to it, as Roland suggested, until I read the comment below one particular image with one comment that sets off alarm bells.

Forevermrshughes commented, "Bitch doesn't know how to take a hint." I want to throw a fit, but what good will that do? I sense whoever this is is closer than we would like. There are many more, but that's the one that bothers me the most. I close the apps.

I feel safe with Roland and am comfortable with the relationship we are building, full of passion, although we never know what is next, recalling the events of last night. I want it all, but am I asking for too much? He knows what it does to me when he places his hand on the small of my back—the largeness of him makes the smallness of me feel safe and protected. He admits he loves the passion we bring out in each other, not just in the bed but in all we say and do. I think he loves the competitiveness, and we bring just enough upheaval to each other to keep it interesting, including Roland and his fandom, me and my book, and social media.

I am unsure how long I've been sitting on the balcony listening to the waves, lost in thought when Roland steps out with a bloody Mary in his hand. "Good morning, Superman. Do you have your phone with you?" I ask cheerfully as my slight headache allows.

"No. It's by the bed."

"Grab it before you sit down if you don't mind." He looks at me questioningly, knowing how much I hate the phone.

Sitting down beside me, he chirps, "Good morning."

"You need to check your accounts and pay attention to anything forevermrshughes comments, please."

"I want to apologize for last night. I am sorry. I never want to make you think I want to possess you. I do, however, want to protect you. I've never wanted to protect anyone or anything more," he looks up from his phone and smiles.

"You have nothing to apologize for. I'm grateful that you do want to protect me. I've never had anyone protect me, Roland. I enjoyed seeing your protective side, and Derek got what he deserved. He'll think twice about ever grabbing me again should he see us. I don't understand why he did all that yesterday."

"It was worth punching the bastard. Although I need to ensure I see Maggie again before I leave the country and apologize again." He sips his bloody Mary.

"I don't want to think about it anymore. Today is the last day here in California that my schedule is free before flying home. Are you interested in spending the day with me?"

"I can probably be persuaded." He sips his drink. "What do you have in mind?"

"I want to go riding."

"Now you're talking my language. Let's do it. I'm ready to go again," he says with the excitement of a child on Christmas morning.

"I know how to ride. I used to have my own Harley, and I still have my license," I inform him.

"I didn't know you ride; you shock me sometimes."

"I bet I do, but what did I do now?"

"You didn't do anything. You're just the whole package, a mixture of fire and holy water," he shakes his head and laughs before continuing, "I'd prefer you ride with me." Roland disappearing back inside looks over his shoulder, "I'll have to surprise you someday."

I crank my head to my right and look over my shoulder and through the door as I speak loudly, "I think you've reached your allowed quota of surprises." I'm not sure what he has in mind, but whatever it is, I am convinced I have asked for it, even begged.

We spend the day on the motorbike riding along the PCH, occasionally stopping to see the sights. I used to live here, so the tourist thing doesn't interest me. Hanging on to his waist all day, lost in my thoughts and him occasionally reaching down and grabbing my calf is all I need for a great day.

"Roland, we can't be here," I tell him as we stroll hand in hand along a private beach; if that isn't romantic enough, he leads me to a secluded area behind one of the largest homes I have ever seen.

"They're friends of mine. It's fine."

As we get closer, I see a white wooden pergola with a table and two chairs in the middle. Tiki lights surround it. The table is covered in a white linen tablecloth with red rose petals scattered around the floor and chairs. I'm stunned when I turn around, throw my body into his arms, and asks, "What is this for? When did you have time to arrange this?"

"It's almost Valentine's Day," he teases. A waiter approaches, carrying a bottle of champagne and two flutes. Soft music begins to play from the speakers. The waiter returns, bringing two preselected meals of Roland's choosing: lobster tails, baked potatoes, and corn on the cob. I stare at him, and there is so much I want to say, but I don't want to ruin this perfect day with unnecessary noise. I love him. I always have, and if I'd not felt the ice melt from around my heart in London, then surely it would now.

Underneath my strong, confident exterior is a woman that

has spent her entire life not believing she is worthy of love. Returning home to see Mom and having to face the men that hurt me have ripped open a wound inside me that I believed was healed. Roland deserves more than I can ever give him. Broken women like me shatter until there is nothing left but sharp pieces on this earth that cut and make others bleed. I know how to be the woman I created—the rigid woman who never bends and is unfeeling. I can do routine, but the feelings Roland is making me feel again—love, trust, passion—are dangerous, and I feel that in my being. I do what I do best, and I swallow the pain. I try to appreciate the man standing before me as he pulls me close, and we dance slowly under the moonlight.

Back at the hotel, at last, I pick up Roland's tie off the chair where it has lain since he wore it to the party last night. Roland doesn't notice what I have in my hand until I walk toward where he sits on the bed. His eyes smile playfully as he slowly shakes his head left to right. I place my hands against both of his shoulders and push him easily back, so he is now lying on the bed. I unbutton his jeans and pull them down along with his boxers until I need to remove his boots.

"Things like this aren't forgotten in the movies," I tease.

Roland snickers and attempts to sit up and remove his boots, but I push him back down and remove them for him. I pull his t-shirt over his head, relieving him of it before rubbing my hands over his hard physique, appreciating each hard muscle. Once I have him out of his clothing, I remove my clothing and straddle him. He wraps his arms around me and kisses my lips, ears, and neck as I lean back. He stops as he sees the bruises left behind on my arms where Derek grabbed me. I watch his expression change from tenderness to concern. He gently touches the marks on my arms and shakes his head.

"It's nothing. Don't worry about it; I've been banged up worse than that." I shake my head, smile, and dismiss it as I reach behind his head and pull his lips down to my breast. His kisses trail off, and he stands up while holding me, turns around, and lays me down, straddling me. He gently moves my left arm above my head and then my right. Each kiss, each touch, is carefully thought out. He loosely wraps the tie around my wrist.

"Now, let's see if you can just lay there and be a good girl. You are not in control. Repeat after me. I am not in control."

I repeat it, "I'm not in control."

"I know it's difficult for you. No touching. No noise."

It takes all the control I have not to move as he nibbles on my earlobe and slowly moves down my neck, where he gently bites and sucks. *Oh, God. Not my neck.* His tongue is in my mouth, owning me. I arch my body toward his. All I can think about is holding on to him and pulling him to me as I fight the urge to touch him. He moves his body farther away from me and loves me with his tongue. My mind races. How can I not move when everything inside me wants to touch him? I have restrained my body as long as I am capable.

"I can't take it. You win. I'm not good at that game." I scream out right before my body releases. He then lowers himself down on me. My body resists him as I spasm from the orgasm he just brought. His own need for satisfaction pushes forward as I wrap my legs around him, and he brings us both to climax—me for the second time. I move my arms around his neck, easily sliding my hands out of the tie. I dig my nails into his back as he collapses on top of me. Perfectly content under the weight of his body, I hug him tighter, not wanting to move until I can't breathe.

He rolls off of me and takes me with him. Lying with my sweaty, breathless body on top of his, I hear his heart pound. I lay in his bed and listen to him breathe; I relive the best day and night of my life, dancing in his arms in the moonlight, then wrapping my arms around his waist as he rides us home on the motorbike. I know I'm not dreaming, but I could die tonight knowing my heart is capable of much more than I ever gave it credit.

I hate that I have to end this before one of us gets hurt. I've been more concerned about him hurting me, but I know what will happen. I will chase him off. Maybe that is what Maggie was trying to hint about last night.

Chapter 11

The Story

This morning is the second in a row I have woken able to stare into Roland's beautiful face. I search his features, his strong square jawline, perfectly shaped nose, and stubble on his unshaven face. I touch the spot on my body, still raw from where his whiskers last rubbed. I watch his chest rise and fall as he inhales all the love and adoration I exhale in his direction. I don't want this moment to end, but we need to make our way to Santa Monica this morning. I nudge my warm body closer to his until we are flesh against flesh. I run my hand along the entire length of his body, memorizing each curve in his muscular legs, chest, abs, and arms if this moment never happens again. He opens his eyes, smiles, and envelopes my body to his. "Good morning," I whisper.

"Good morning, love."

"We have to go to Santa Monica today for the book signing."

"I know, but I had a thought last night. I want to drive to Santa Barbara first and meet your mom," he says in his raspy voice after just waking.

"Santa Barbara is out of our way." I protest.

"What else do you have to do today? It's a beautiful morning for a drive." He pulls my lips to his and kisses me before saying, "We are never in that big of a hurry," as he flips his body on top of mine.

Later, he loads my luggage into the rental car, and we drive north on the PCH. Arriving, Mom meets us outside. "Mom, this is Roland Hughes. Roland, my mother, Sylvia." He hugs her.

"I am surprised you drove back here today, Dahlia. Is everything all right?" Mom asks.

"Yes, Roland wanted to meet you, and I wanted to show him the building site for the lake house. We had a few extra hours but can't stay long."

"I guessed that. Let's ride down." Mom points to the Mule as she climbs behind the wheel, and we get in.

"I want to see," Roland replies. We show him the proposed layout and promise to show him the blueprints when they are finished. "Are you hungry? Would you like to go to lunch?" Roland asks.

"I'd love to go to lunch with you both." Mom laughs as we enter the kitchen. "But I'd prefer to eat here if you don't mind. I made a small brunch after Dahlia called saying you were coming."

"Are you sure you wouldn't rather go out to eat? We don't want to put you out." Roland asks.

"Yes, I'm positive." Mom shows him her shaking hands and then picks up a fork and tries to hold it. "I'd rather not have food down the front of me in public. The attention both of you attract is all I need, photos of me with my front covered in food."

Roland, Mom, and I sit at the kitchen table, visiting and eating my favorite snack foods, including hummus. "Mom, did you receive the results of all the scans your doctor did? What did they say?"

"I was waiting to tell you, Dahlia, but I guess it's as good a time as any. Sorry, Roland, that you need to hear my issues." She looks at me, and I realize I shouldn't have asked her in front of Roland. Mom smiles as she notices me watching her shaky hands and head. "I have what they refer to as progressive supranuclear palsy. It is fast-acting Parkinson's and includes dementia. You need to look it up, and it will tell you more, but that's all I want to say about it right now. Okay?"

"Of course, Mom. We understand." I change the subject. "What have you been doing with your time?" I don't want to press her for answers. I'll research it on my own.

"Since you were here only a couple of days ago, not much has changed, except I joined a book club, and I have been reading a lot and keeping my mind busy."

"Awesome, I know a great author." I tease.

"Me too, but I've read it."

"Not my second book," I tell her as we finish our lunch.

"Really? I didn't know you were writing a second book." Her expression tells me she wants to ask if it will stir up trouble, but she doesn't.

"I can't very well tell your story and not my own, Mom. I'll send you one if it doesn't take a year to read."

"I couldn't sit and read it with Cameron sitting there. That would've been hard to explain."

"You mean Bob?" I laugh. "Who is Cameron? You have a new boyfriend?" Mom looks at me, confused.

"I meant Bob. Who did I say?" I glance at Roland as he shrugs his shoulders.

"Cameron," I answer.

"I don't know a Cameron. Maybe my mind slips a little bit." Mom dismisses her words while I hide my concern. I clean off the table and load the dishwasher while watching Mom and Roland get to know each other. Their visit allows me to watch her without making her self-conscious. Finally, having my mother back only to discover her debilitating disease is heartbreaking. She is determined to live alone, but it doesn't take much to see; it won't be long before that choice is not hers to make. "It's a beautiful day, and I'd like to spend it outside if you don't mind," Mom extends her arm for him to escort her.

"Sounds like a great idea," I agree until we are all three greeted by Daniel stepping down from his truck. Mom glances around before she turns to go back inside. "Give me a minute." Looking over my shoulder, I tell Roland.

Daniel takes extra-long steps to shorten the distance between us. "Are you all right? I saw the social media post of what happened." I glance over my shoulder as Roland reaches me in record timing and stands between Daniel and me. "Look, Roland, that's your name, right?" Roland nods his head yes. "I'm Daniel, Dahlia's ex-husband." Daniel extends his hand to shake Roland's while still looking at me.

"Yes, I recognize you from the photos of you and Whisky Girl having dinner the other night." Roland accepts his hand, and their faces search for my response. I smile.

"Whisky Girl?" Daniel says sarcastically and looks at me for an explanation, but I ignore him. Roland does, too. Daniel continues, "I'm not here to cause problems. I'm just worried about Dahlia and want to check on her. She isn't answering her cell phone." Daniel shoots me a look of disappointment.

It occurs to me why he is here. *Please don't say anything about Derek.* I reach up to touch Daniel's arm, thinking he'll accept my non-verbal cue, but before I can reach him, he tells Roland, "I hope you beat the living shit out of the rapist." There it is, dropped right before God and everyone.

"What the hell are you talking about, Daniel?" Roland's face tells me he has put two and two together and got twenty-two. Daniel's expression tells me he knows he stuck his foot in his mouth and shouldn't have said anything. They are both looking at me.

135

"I'm sorry, Dahlia. I didn't know you hadn't told him."

Roland looks at me and wants answers, but I freeze. I don't want to speak the words; it was my fault. I put myself in that position. I don't know what happened to me. How do I say all that?

"Roland, can I have a word with Daniel in private? I will tell you everything tonight. I promise."

"Are you kidding me?" He reluctantly takes approximately ten steps away from us as he faces me and watches.

"I'm sorry, Dahlia. Never in a million years did I guess he didn't know. When I saw all the photos, it made me sick. I could check on you in person or locate the bastard and kill him. When you didn't answer your phone, I was freaking out."

"How do you know where Mom lives, or do I need even to ask? Did she tell you I was coming to town in the first place?" I look toward the house and Mom, staring out the back door. "You are how Bob knew I was in town, too?"

"I've stayed close to your parents, Dahlia. What's the big deal?"

"Nothing, I guess. Roland took him down quickly. You'd have been happy to see how he handled it. Never in a million years would I have ever expected to run into that man again, and something tells me it wasn't by accident. I didn't have a minute alone to take your call. I haven't had the time to fill Roland in on a decade of my chaos, but I should tell him now." I reach up and hug Daniel. "I'll call and talk to you when I get home, okay?"

"Promise?"

"Yes," I promise. Daniel waves as he drives away, leaving behind unwanted words.

Roland uses his long legs to be at my side in about three steps. He wraps his arms around me and leads me to the swing. I lean against him as he rocks us, "I will tell you everything. I briefly thought about it the other night. Remember when I asked you about men hurting me?"

"Yes. And now the question you asked makes a lot more sense."

"Let's talk about it tonight. Right now, I don't want Mom to worry. Let's finish this visit and get me to the signing." I tap his leg and kiss him before I stand up and go back inside to tell Mom it's safe to come out.

* * *

It is a quiet ride to Santa Monica as Roland gives me space and time. I contain my tears and emotions the best I can while trying to come up with words to describe something that happened to me. The fans are thrilled to see Roland has accompanied me to the book signing. I love it when all eyes fix on him and not on me. I watch him intently as we greet the fans. He charms each one as we sign autographs. My mind drifts to a place where Roland and I are alone, where the world can't touch us.

As he pulls the car into a parking spot at the Shangri-La hotel in Santa Monica, the heaviness weighs on me. The laughter and light-heartedness I felt only the day before yesterday seem a lifetime ago. Leaving him and my mom tomorrow is heavy on my heart. My thoughts drift to things I need to take care of, my book tour, getting help for my mother, and wondering if whoever wrote the Dear Jane letter all those years ago could foresee something I couldn't. How will I tell him what it is I need to say? How will I deal with a long-distance relationship now that I have fallen in love with him all over?

"You here with me, love?" Roland asks as he hands me a drink.

I stare into the face of a man I believe to be perfect, and I am grateful to have him back in my life, "Yes, I'm sorry. Just heavy in thought, I guess."

He touches my face, presses his warm lips to my cold lips, and whispers against them, "I love you. Even the broken bits of you I love. I know some of those bits are my doing, and I promise to do everything to mend each one."

My kiss becomes hungry, and I wrap my arms around his neck, trying to pull him to me, but he resists me. "We have to talk. I need to know what happened. I know you want to love me without words, but sometimes they are needed. Sex isn't the only way to show love, and I'm sorry you've been hurt and believe that is the only way you are lovable. You are lovable just the way you are."

Again, I cry and scold myself for it. "I'm afraid you won't want me anymore after telling my stories."

"That is ridiculous. Tell me this story first. We'll save the rest for another time. We have a lifetime. I don't need to know everything, love, but obviously, this is something I should've known."

"The incident happened a little over a year after I left England and moved back home. I'd been on anti-depressants, mood stabilizers, and anxiety meds for over a year. I was severely depressed and didn't want to leave my house. I wish I wouldn't have either. My friend, Karen, from college, called and said she'd bumped into another friend of ours and wanted to invite me to come to Hollywood and stay with her for the weekend and attend the premiere of The Twilight Saga: Eclipse. I was so excited that I would meet the stars of the movie. Karen even drove to Montecito to pick me up. I agreed, believing it would be good for me to get out and do something fun. Do you remember the gown I bought and wore to the Air Force ball we attended?"

"Yes, of course. You looked amazing," Roland replies.

Taking a drink, I stand, pace the room, and glance out the window, eventually settling in a chair opposite the bed before I dived off the deep end of my story. "Well, I wore that. It still had the small wine stain from when we clinked glasses, and the wine splashed on me, remember?"

"Yes."

"Karen drove straight to the premiere, and my overnight bag was in her car. I never made it to Karen's house, which is a good thing, it turns out. It was amazing mingling with the stars on the red carpet while following behind Karen. The after-party was memorable until it wasn't. I was having a great time, too great of a time, I guess, but I swear I only had three drinks within three hours. I was introduced to a Hollywood producer." I am looking down while I tell him.

He knows what I am about to say when I look up and see his face tighten. "Go ahead. Please tell me Derek Duncan isn't your friend's father."

"I wish I could. I remember Karen and I were talking to a group of people she knew when Derek handed us glasses of champagne and made a toast. That was my third glass since I arrived for the premiere. One of the men asked Karen to dance, and Derek asked me. I agreed, even though it was a slow dance. He reached behind me and pulled the one pin from my hair, letting it fall around my waist. I pushed away from him, but he held on to me, so I pushed away again and walked back to Karen's table. I talked, laughed, and danced with others, and I remember fine. But I don't remember anything after leaving the party. When I woke up, it was light outside. I looked around and realized I was in a hotel room naked and alone."

I stand up, grab a tissue, and sit beside Roland. "I called Karen's number immediately, but she didn't answer. I was terrified that whose ever room I was in would return, so I found my gown on the floor, and when I attempted to put it on, it was torn. It looked like it was ripped off of me. I couldn't wear it."

Roland holds my hand and adjusts his position. I climb to the center of the bed, sit cross-legged, take a deep breath, and continue, "I put on the big white robe. My phone was in my clutch, and I called my friend Daniel to come and get me. I grabbed my dress, then went to the pool and waited. Being in a robe wouldn't look odd if I was by the pool. When Daniel pulled into the parking lot, I got in his truck before he could even get out. He drove a block away, then parked. I begged him not to return to the hotel, but he was furious. I don't know what happened, and I never asked, but Daniel returned thirty minutes later and drove me to the VA hospital, where I stayed for a week." I climb off the bed, stand in front of the window with my back to it, and face Roland. "I hate him for showing up on the beach and bringing all this back to me. I hate that he touched my skin. I hate that he looked into my face and saw my vulnerability. I've never forgotten it, but I didn't have to deal with it or speak about it before. I hate that I don't know what happened that night."

Roland moves close to me, attempting to pull me into his arms, but I step away and sit back in the chair. He sits opposite me. I continued, "They checked me into the mental health ward after treating me in the ER, where they did a rape kit. If raped, my attacker wore a condom. They ran all the tests, pregnancy, and diseases, all negative. There is no way to describe how terrifying it was to tell doctors and the police that I had no idea if I was raped. If I was, I had no idea by whom, only that I woke up in a hotel that way. I called Karen to ask where she had disappeared, and she reminded me that she was ready to leave. She said I was dancing with the producer, Derek Duncan, and he said he would give me a ride to her house. I didn't remember any of it. She did not mention that producer was her father until I called her a week later and asked her to bring me my overnight bag. When she did, I told her what had happened, and we had an awful fight. She and I have never spoken again, but I discovered that Derek Duncan was divorced shortly after that, and his wife got millions in their settlement."

"I'm going to kill him." Roland is off the bed and out of the hotel room door before I can stop him. Yelling for him to come back repeatedly, he finally does. He holds me, and I can feel the tears on his face mix with my own.

"Listen to me. The VA said I probably blacked out because I mixed prescription meds and alcohol because they didn't find anything questionable in my blood system. I quit taking the meds and didn't drink again for years. Still, I didn't rip off my dress; I am sure of that. It was nearly eleven years ago. It is over and done. I've never allowed myself to get into a predicament like that or seen him again until he appeared on the beach."

Roland pulls me to him as I tell him, "The calmness of you quiets the chaos in me. I hate losing you, but you must let me go, Roland. I've made too many bad choices and mistakes. I am no good for you. I do have issues, as the note said." He dismisses my words.

I've spoken the words aloud and see my reflection in his eyes. Hopefully, his opinion of me is kinder than that of my own. I tell him, "I'm finished talking about this. No more talking about this, and I don't want to talk again." I shower and climb into bed, knowing I must end this with Roland. He deserves someone who isn't damaged.

Roland and I make love tonight. I give up control as he covers my body in kisses and gentle caresses. I pull him close to me. If I could crawl inside his skin, I would. I love him enough to let him go. Afterward, he holds me close as I fall asleep in his arms, and I hear him whisper, "I love every inch of you, even your scars, are beautiful." I remain silent. "I'm not letting you go, and you're not going anywhere love."

The following morning, I wake up to Roland staring at me. "Do you have to leave today?"

"No, but you have work to do, and I've finished what I came here to do. Frankly, I'd feel safer in a state where Derek and Bob don't reside."

"I get that. What time is your flight?"

"Three."

"Great. Let's go riding and out to lunch."

"Sounds like a wonderful day."

Chapter 12

Skyfall

March 3rd

I choose a beautiful red silky gown that stops mid-calf, fitting tightly across my breast, with an off-the-shoulder ruffle. I didn't anticipate being so nervous that my legs might fail to hold me. I spend the first fifteen minutes of the show in my dressing room wearing noise-canceling headphones until an assistant retrieves me and leads me to a spot where I am told to stand and wait until I hear my name. Standing behind a big blue curtain, I pray I don't misstep and fall.

"She is a *New York Times* best-selling author. Please welcome, Dahlia Frost." I expect to step up on a stage, but Jimmy is standing near a small table. I wave to the audience as Jimmy greets me, offers a reassuring hug, and pulls my chair out. We are sitting across from each other at what appears to be a miniature version of a ping pong table. The center has a divider with only a small hole cut out. Jimmy sits on the other side of the table and peers through the hole at me.

"Have you seen this game played?" Jimmy asks.

"Yes, but why me?" I didn't know I was playing a game.

"Let's get started. Pick a number, pick up the coordinated box, and bring it back over."

Instructed to remove the item from the box and not let Jimmy see it, I reach into it and remove what appears to be a video game. "I have a video game with corndogs as the cartridge."

"I don't believe you," Jimmy says, and he is correct. I have a video game with actual videos.

Jimmy picks a box. "I have a vase of grilled cheeses made to look like a flower arrangement."

I believe he is mocking my corndog idea. "I don't believe you," I respond as he laughs and holds up a flower arrangement made of grilled cheeses. Two strikes.

It's Jimmy's turn again since he's two out of three. He reaches into the third box and states, "This is a scotch whiskey bottle."

"Is it full? Because I could use a dram," I joke.

"I could, too," he laughs as he speaks, and I'm reminded why I love this show. I feel my body relax, and I laugh at my joke. He continues, "You're funny. No, it is empty, and it has photos on the inside."

"I think you're lying."

"It has photos of you and a man inside it." Jimmy's face is puzzled.

"Is he good-looking?" I pause and shake my head, assuring myself there is no way Roland would pull off another grand entrance. I've avoided Roland's calls, but I've sent back quick texts to answer his questions. I'm attempting to put space between us. I reply, "I got you this time; I don't believe you."

Jimmy stands before announcing, "Welcome back, Roland Hughes, everybody." The audience lets out screams and whistles. I, on the other hand, do not scream and whistle. I want to beat Roland senseless. I turn toward the curtain just as Roland walks out from behind it, making uppercut moves with his arms and hands. His smile is dazzling as he waves and greets the audience. What am I talking about? His entire essence is dazzling. The effect he has on me is evident as I tremble. I don't know why I'm shocked that he has pulled off another grand entrance because he has a knack for pulling off the greatest of reveals.

He approaches, hugs me, and grabs my hand to hold as he escorts me to the chairs on the stage. He shakes Jimmy's hand before Jimmy breaks for a commercial. I immediately whisper in Roland's ear, "I can't believe you did this."

Jimmy overhears and assures me, "It's fine. Take our lead."

Staring at me, Roland then whispers, "I told you you're not going anywhere."

"Welcome back to *The Tonight Show*. I'm talking with author Dahlia Frost and actor Roland Hughes." The audience applauds.

Speaking first, I ask, "Did I win that game?" Laughing, Jimmy informs me that I did not.

"Welcome, Dahlia. It is a pleasure to meet you. You've never been here before, have you?"

"No, but I am thrilled to be here and shocked Roland is here with me." I reach over and grip Roland's hand briefly.

"Good. You were looking a little nervous over there."

"That's because I was losing."

Jimmy pulls a copy of *Daddy Issues* and stands it on the desk. "Let me ask you about your best-selling novel. It was an immediate bestseller, which isn't common, especially for a debut novelist. What can you tell me about the book?"

I give a short description of the book, including the part where Emma leaves the love of her life, Joshua, behind. The audience applauds and chants Roland's name. I can work with this as I smile and clap for Roland. "After returning to the States, Emma is determined to find out why she has repressed memories and what those memories are. She quickly discovers that some things are best left buried. The story depicts Emma's struggles and creative ways to handle the dysfunction in her life, which eventually spills over to her bed."

"We've heard the rumors about the bed part involving the man sitting to your right. You based Joshua on your past relationship with Roland. The ladies in the audience think that is true even if it isn't." The women clap and whistle.

"Yes, it is true. Roland and I dated when we were young. He surprised me at my book signing, much like he has done tonight. He loves big reveals." I smile the biggest "fake" smile I can manage.

"I am interested in the newly released information concerning you. I watched the interview discussing the Halsey heiress story. I also read an article where you said, 'I've gone from invisible to visible overnight.' If you don't mind, tell me the Halsey heiress story," Jimmy suggests.

"Sure. It's quite a story. In the novel, I write about my father, who died after the accident, leaving me with no memory of six years of my life. After discovering what was missing from my memory, I moved to New York. I can hardly believe that was six years ago. Anyway, I wrote my novel the first year after I moved here. I queried agents, received rejections, and lived off my VA disability when an attorney came to my apartment." Pausing, I jest, "Men seem to pop up unexpectedly." Roland and Jimmy laugh. I continue with the story, "I thought he was someone coming to repossess my car." It wasn't that far-fetched. "Instead, my grandmother passed, and the executors of her estate had been searching for over a year for her heir. I remember seeing the news reports and the tabloids, but I had no idea. My mother had never told me my father was that Halsey. So, I tried to keep it quiet as long as possible; it is like winning the lottery, as you can imagine. I didn't want people coming out

146

of the woodwork. My attorney did a great job protecting my identity, and of course, I published *Daddy Issues* under a pen name."

"Wow. You won't believe this, but I discovered we are cousins." Jimmy laughs at his joke.

"Well, Jimmy, I wish I'd have known that when I struggled."

"Roland, welcome back. Long time no see." As he looks back at me, Jimmy says, "You were wearing noise-canceling headphones because we didn't want you to know Roland was here."

"I didn't realize that wasn't common practice. I was enjoying the music." I respond.

Jimmy directs his attention back to Roland. "In the show's first half, we discussed your whiskey business ventures and what you've been doing with your time. Why the surprise for Dahlia?"

"As I said earlier, I just finished filming a new movie. For the film before this one, I worked in Budapest and India, but the most recent project took me to Mexico, Austria, and London. After that, I discovered Whisky Girl was also in London, and I surprised her at her book signing. Unless someone has read *Daddy Issues* and placed me as Joshua, they might believe we just met. But Whisky Girl and I have known each other for nineteen years. We were apart nearly thirteen of those, but once I discovered Frances Slater and Dahlia Frost were the same people and the character of Joshua wasn't murdered in her novel, I thought it might be safe to reconnect." Roland jokes, causing the audience to applaud and laugh. I laugh, secretly believing he most likely did wonder if it was safe.

"I understand you brought a trailer for us, but before we get to that, I want to ask you a question. And don't either of you shoot the messenger. For years, Roland, you've been asked about your relationship status, but you've kept quiet, leaving your personal life a mystery. Then, the Internet is broken when fans post pictures of you stunning Dahlia at her book signing. Then, you're seen together around London and on vacation in California. What made you both choose to be this visible?"

"We're not trying to be visible. We're just living our lives outside, especially since the pandemic and the quarantine. I surprised her tonight because I know how nervous she is over the publicity she and the book have recently received. When I discovered she and I were scheduled to appear on the same night, I wanted to be here to support her."

Reaching over and squeezing his hand, I tell him, "Thank you. I appreciate that."

"Dahlia, why does he call you Whisky Girl? After the whiskey?"

"I happened before the whiskey. So technically, the whiskey is named after me."

"Roland, I wanted to ask you a question before Dahlia came out, but I'll ask now. I hear your name is top on the list to be the next James Bond. How do you feel about that?" Jimmy asks.

"I think any actor who looks good in a suit has his name on the next James Bond list. It's been years now that the list has been going around. I believe I heard they already hired the next Bond." The audience lets out a few boos. Jimmy and I smile in agreement.

"When the series I worked on while living in Hollywood ended, I took on a new role. After it is released, I will start filming on *Daddy Issues* early next year."

Jimmy asks, "Which movie clip did you bring for us tonight? I know this is coming out in theaters soon."

"I have a surprise for all of you. I spent my entire afternoon on the phone asking permission to release this film trailer a few months early."

Jimmy looks at the camera and the crowd, "I have no idea

what we're about to see, but we have a sneak peek of Roland's new movie; let's watch," Jimmy announces while looking at Roland quizzically. I shrug my shoulders and lift my hands.

The clip begins, and the original theme music for James Bond by Monty Norman and John Barry starts to play. I jump up from my seat, throw my arms around him, and sit back down. Jimmy jumps up and comes around the desk to shake Roland's hand. The film trailer for the new James Bond film plays, and the room falls silent until the end when it explodes again.

"Oh my God, I didn't know. How did you keep this secret, Roland? I'm honored you revealed this exciting news here on *The Tonight Show*. I am shocked, wow! What an exciting year for you—for both of you." Jimmy is on his feet and clapping. Roland squeezes my hand.

"You have no idea, buddy. It's been a phenomenal year," Roland tells Jimmy.

"Talk about a mic drop. Thank you, Roland, and thank you, Dahlia. Congratulations on finding each other again. Dahlia, congratulations on your book and all future successes. Congratulations, Roland, on your success and being the next James Bond. Damn, I'm still overwhelmed. Best wishes, bud. Dahlia Frost and Roland Hughes, everybody."

* * *

I'm aware Roland knows the price of his celebrity. He, too, had done pretty well at keeping his private life private until he brought me back into it, so I decided to follow his lead regarding the paparazzi. "Why on earth did you surprise me on national television?" I ask him.

"As I said, when I discovered we were both scheduled to appear on the same night, I wanted to support you and the book. After all, it won't be long before I am promoting *Daddy Issues*, the movie. I gave it a jump start. Besides, I knew once I dropped the James Bond bomb, the world would quit focusing on you and me and direct their attention back to our careers."

"Sounds good to me. You know more about this than I do."

After our appearance and the show's adrenaline rush, Roland is ready to celebrate and instructs the driver to take us to his favorite restaurant in New York, Sona's. I mean, why not, right? The only people who don't know that he and I are friends are people who don't know who either of us is.

We know we have a four-hour window before the show airs, and Roland's big news creates a frenzy within his fandom. We have a wonderful, relaxing dinner and afterward, I suggest we go to a private club where I like to go occasionally, similar to Cheers, where everyone knows my name. Roland is familiar with the club but protests since it is not a scheduled stop, and we don't have bodyguards. "I'm surprised you want to go anywhere."

"I know. I think it's the adrenaline of tonight. It has been such an amazing night, and I'm having so much fun. I learn quickly; I've seen the crowds you attract, so it's okay if we can't go."

Roland clicks his tongue, looks left to right, taps his fingers on his leg, then hesitantly agrees, "Jackson, take us to the club." The driver nods and pulls away from the restaurant.

"Really? Are you sure, Roland?" I ask.

"Just for one drink like we did in London. In and out, okay? You know we'll have to do a photo or two."

"Thank you." I squeeze his hand. Little did we know, a fan posted a video of *The Tonight Show* appearance on social media. When we exit the club and are a few steps outside the entrance doors, the paparazzi and fans pour down on him like rain from the sky. He holds my hand but we are separated in the push and shove. I hear him call my name.

The flashes blind me right before my stiletto's heel catch in the sidewalk crack. I try to counterbalance, but it's too late; the calf-length dress I chose for tonight doesn't allow a wide stance. I attempt to stop my fall by grabbing onto whomever I can as I go down. I scream out Roland's name. The crowd shifts as I land on my bottom first, then fall back bumping my head on someone's legs. I put my hands out to break my fall, but they are trampled. Immediately, I pull them in and cover my face until I am kicked in the side and instinctively reach to cover that pain. I'm not sure how I hear the driver call out Roland's name above the crowd of screaming fans, but I do.

He yells, "I got you; where is Ms. Frost?"

A woman and I meet eyes as she attempts to keep me from being squashed. She instantly steps over and straddles me before screaming, "Help."

I hear Roland's voice, "Dahlia, Dahlia!" The woman extends her hand to me. I reach up to grab it, but in that instant, I watch as Roland picks up the woman and removes her from above me, then he bends down and picks me up. The driver pushes people out of the way to open the SUV door. Roland places me inside and climbs in beside me. I gasp for air, tears stain my face, and I see mascara drops on my blood-stained dress. My hands are trembling, and when I look down at them, they are both scraped and bleeding. I see a large spot of blood soaking through my dress where I was kicked. The driver speeds away. I look into Roland's face; he is terrified and shaken. "I'm sorry. I tried to hang on to you as we were pulled apart. I love you. I'm so sorry."

Sitting still, I place my bloody hand over his heart and bend my head into the crease of his armpit. "Roland, we need to go to the emergency room. You're hurt, too." He shakes his head no, but I see the cut on his forehead dripping blood down his face and onto his shirt. He wipes the blood away, smearing it across his head. He instructs the driver to take us to the hospital. When I step out, I realize I can't put weight on my right ankle, so Roland again carries me. He and I are placed in a room to wait.

"Speak to me. How are you? I see your hands, a cut on your side. Did you hit your head?"

"No, I will be fine."

The doctor enters, looks at Roland's forehead, and administers four stitches. The nurse helping him recognizes Roland, "Aren't you...?" Roland nods yes. The nurse turns to me, "You're Dahlia...?"

I wave my hand to shoo them both out. "Get out of the room, Roland. Take it out of the room." After finishing the last stitch, the nurse looked at the doctor, who had just removed his gloves. He nods for her to leave.

"I'd like to talk to Ms. Frost alone, please," the doctor states. Roland bends down, kisses my forehead, and leaves the room, followed closely by the nurse.

I overhear the nurse, "I'm so sorry. I didn't mean to upset her."

"You didn't. I did," Roland replies.

The doctor smiles, "Let's start with you telling me what happened." Immediately I cry as I describe what happened, how I felt at the time, and how I feel right now. "It was a terrifying incident," I tell him as I end the story by letting my head fall against the pillow.

He leaves the room, and I listen as he tells Roland, "Let me get her labs and x-rays taken and her wounds cleaned up, then I am sure she'll be in a better mood. She's shaken up and a bit battered, but she'll be fine."

I listen to Roland's voice, and it soothes me. God knows why it helps me, but it does. He peeks into the room, "Can I come back in?"

Waving him in, I say, "I'm sorry, Roland. This was my fault." There is a television somewhere close, and we hear *The Tonight Show* begin. Roland smiles at me, and I can't help but smile back. "Go watch it, babe."

He shakes his head, "No. I know what happens." Roland holds my hand and sits down beside the bed.

An hour later, with an x-ray taken, my wounds cleaned and bandaged, the doctor enters the room, "Ms. Frost, would you prefer we speak alone, or can your boyfriend be here?"

"It's fine; he can stay," I answer as a nurse puts a splint on my ankle before leaving the room.

"Your ankle is not broken. That is the good news. I have some news that only you can decide if it is positive or negative. Your lab work came back with a positive pregnancy." The room goes silent except for the doctor's words ricocheting off the walls and bouncing around in my head as I look into Roland's eyes, his expression mirroring my own. "I'm assuming this is shocking news from both your expressions."

I nod and thank the doctor as I am handed a set of crutches. No other words are spoken until we get into the SUV, depart the hospital and drive to my apartment. "Are you all right?" Roland asks.

"I'll tell you when we get home, all right?" I answer and sit in my thoughts and silence. The driver pulls into my parking garage. Roland carries me to the elevator, and the driver takes my crutches and Roland's bag. When the elevator opens to my apartment, the lights instantly come on. Roland steps out with me in his arms and looks around, not knowing where to take me. "Straight through the foyer and to the right," I instruct him. He lays me on the sectional, excuses the driver, and locks out the elevator.

He returns and sits beside me on the sectional. He and I stare out the floor-to-ceiling windows over the city's lights. I'm afraid of what will come out of my mouth if I speak. "Roland, can we discuss this tomorrow after we sleep? I'm exhausted and emotionally spent."

"Sounds like a great idea. Point me in the right direction." He picks me up, and I direct us up the staircase to the master suite, where he sits me on the loveseat. My mind is racing as I remove, then throw my left shoe across the room, wondering where my right shoe has gone. I stand on my left leg, balancing myself against the loveseat, and pull my dress up to my hips. Roland appears back in the bedroom to help me, gently unzipping the back of my dress. When finished, he sweeps me into his arms, carries me to the bathroom, and then quietly closes the door behind him as he leaves.

Immediately, seeing the woman staring back at me with a tear-streaked face and unable to stop crying, I gasp for breath. I attempt to calm myself by reaching for a hot washcloth, placing it over my face, and wiping away the memory of tonight with the makeup. I glimpse the bandage on my lower left side covering the gouge caused by a high heel shoe and lift it to see the damage. I brush my hair and teeth staring at the bandages on my hands. Roland opens the door and steps in, moving to my side and wrapping his arms around me, holding me up both physically and emotionally before carrying me to bed. Gently he lays me down and covers me up before disappearing into the bathroom. My eyes follow him as I listen to every sigh, thump, and quickened heartbeat. It is the noisiest room I've ever been in for a room surrounded by silence. Neither of us knows what to say or is afraid to say anything. He crawls into bed beside me and gently pulls me to him. I feel his breath in my ear as he whispers, but his words bounce off me, echoing off the walls, "Are we not going to talk about this tonight?"

"Tomorrow. I don't have the words or the energy," I whisper, kiss his lips, roll over, adjust my pillow, and touch off my lamp. I pretend to be asleep as I lay there and listen to the video he is watching of our incident tonight that someone recorded and posted. My tears silently fall. I don't necessarily want a baby, but I damn sure don't want to lose another one. I've been telling myself everything happens for a reason, and tonight has changed two things: I will never be put in another situation where this can happen again, and I will protect this baby with my life and Roland's.

Chapter 13

Black Dahlias

The following morning, I wake to the smell of food. That is an unusual event in my house since I seldom cook. I sit up and manage the crutches well enough to make it to the bathroom, but I yell for Roland to help me down the stairs. He picks me up, carries me to the kitchen, and then continues making omelets. I didn't know I was hungry until I smelled the food. Once situated, I look up at the television just in time to see clips of *The Tonight Show* followed by clips of the mob that almost trampled me. I lean in and watch as the video shows me going down screaming while the person behind the camera screams my name. It's the same woman who stepped over me to prevent further harm. "Roland, I know it happened, and believe me, I feel the effects, even more this morning, but I still can't believe it."

"I can't believe it either. If I had known something like this would happen, I'd have never surprised you on air. Maybe I should've anticipated the response."

"This wasn't your fault. I'm the one who wanted to go to the club and finish our celebration. Every time I open up and enjoy my life or let go of control, something happens, but I will never make that mistake again. I've just begun to live again, and we're not going to stop living. I've learned a valuable lesson, and the next time you say we shouldn't, I will listen, but we had every right to celebrate your incredible success. I just don't understand how anyone could've known we were at that club unless someone inside the club set off a bat signal."

Roland carries breakfast plates, juice, and coffee for each of us over to the table. When he sits down, he reaches for my hand. "I am so sorry you were hurt. Anyone with a cell phone camera could upload a picture of us. I knew better."

I squeeze his hand, "I know, but that is why I chose that club. I've gone there many times. I know you would never put us in a position like that, and I promise I will be more cautious and never ask such a thing of you again, especially now that I am pregnant."

"Oh, thank God, you brought the pregnancy up. I've been awake all night thinking about this. I can't believe it. Aren't you on birth control?"

I pause, shake my head, staring into his eyes, and stop chewing while holding my fork midway between my plate and mouth. "No, I thought you were."

Roland smirks at me. "I didn't mean it's your responsibility, Smartass. I meant I saw you take your pill at night before we went to bed."

"I'm as shocked as you. I, too, was awake most of the night, and I can only think that I didn't take them long enough before I hopped into bed with you. I had no reason to be on birth control before that. After returning to New York, I got back on them and took my first one when I arrived in California a week before my trip to Malibu and into your arms." I stare into his face and change the subject. "Will you get me some ketchup for my eggs, please?" Roland nods and gets ketchup for my eggs as I continue to mumble and calculate dates in my head. Roland

and I cover our eggs in ketchup and devour the delicious omelet.

"Dahlia, from now on, you nor I will go anywhere without a bodyguard while here in the States. It isn't as intense in Scotland. I want you to consider coming to Scotland and staying with me. I haven't sorted anything else out, but I know I want you with me and safe.

"I won't pack up and move, but I will stay with you when you are there."

"I want to have the baby in Scotland, too. What do you think of that?"

"Roland, I don't know about that yet. Citizenship isn't something I want to ponder this morning. My head is already full, and it's only 8:00 a.m. Please tell me how you feel about this pregnancy?"

"I'm going to be truthful, I don't know. I'm shocked. It's not like I began this year thinking I would end it as a father, but I did begin it knowing I wanted you no matter the cost. I'm happy, I think, but it scares me, and with all that craziness surrounding us right now, I'm even more scared that I won't be near you to protect you."

"That's how I feel too. I'm just happy we'll face it all together." I smile.

After breakfast, I spend the rest of my day lazy with my foot propped up and binge-watching *Outlander*. I've never watched it. If I have to be stowed up, it's the best time because, in two days, apparently the new season begins. Roland is in the office on his phone and computer all day with his business manager and agents about personal and television appearances and interview requests. His big reveal has broken the Internet and the entertainment world.

Charlotte arrives carrying a sack and a cardboard drink carrier with three coffees from my favorite coffee shop down the street. "Roland called and said you need a visitor and coffee. And since I decided to play hooky with you, I meant to bring you a bag of fan mail but forgot it, so Olivia will be here in a second to drop that off." She hands me my latte and muffin, then looks over her shoulder before taking Roland's coffee upstairs to the office for him, "Okay?"

The elevator opens again, and Olivia arrives, setting my mailbag down on the coffee table. "I'm so sorry, Dahlia," she expresses before sitting on the couch. She immediately answers her ringing phone and says, "Bloody hell, Dahlia. I have to go. The paparazzi downstairs want information about your incident. Don't fret; I will tell them to bugger off." Blowing a kiss, she walks out of the apartment when Charlotte comes back downstairs and plops beside me.

"I watched the replay of the incident on television, and I'm sorry." She stares at the paused picture screen, "Oh my God, you're watching *Outlander*. What do you think so far?"

"You told me I had to because the new season will begin. I just started it, so I don't know." Charlotte keeps asking questions, curious about my injuries. I show her my side and hands, and ankle.

She comments on the mailbag, "Olivia was here, already?"

"Here and gone." Then I ask her, "Hey, listen, this is important. Did you know Roland was scheduled to appear on *The Tonight Show,* and do you think Olivia was made aware and failed to tell me? I'd have asked her, but she was called out the second she got here."

"No, I think your boyfriend wanted to surprise you, so no one, including you, was told, but I will talk to her and Jamie. I think one of your publicists should have been aware of who else was appearing. Dahlia, most authors don't get that sort of publicity, so I'm assuming because of the newsworthiness of you and Roland and the Halsey heiress publicity, you were invited onto the show to begin with."

As he descends the stairs, Roland speaks, "I knew you were scheduled to be on, so someone knew on your end, but that is normal. It isn't because we were on together. It's because I revealed the movie and the trailer. We should've just come home after the taping. I knew better."

The buzzer sounds, and Roland answers the door. "Mr. Hughes, I have a delivery for Ms. Frost." I hear Sam, the concierge, voice.

When Roland rounds the corner with a bouquet of black dahlias and sets them on the kitchen island, I gasp, "What the hell is that? Who would send me black dahlias?" It takes me a few minutes to digest the threat delivered to my door. Of course, it's a threat.

Roland pulls the attached card from the bouquet and brings it to me before saying, "I'll be right back." He is on the elevator and gone before I can reply. Charlotte's fearful expression matches my own. I am frightened at the symbolism of these flowers, and I am positive that is the exact response the sender wants me to have. First the note, then the social media comments, then Bob's suggestion Daniel kill me, and then Bob following me. Only a sick mind would take an old murder case where a young woman was bisected at the waist and left in a park in Los Angeles who was known as the Black Dahlia and entwine my name to the flower and send it to me. With shaky hands, I open the attached card.

Roses are Red
Violets are Blue
Black Dahlias die
Then are cut in two.

I hand the card to Charlotte. She is as stunned and shaken up as I am. Roland returns to the apartment with the delivery service's name feeling confident until I hand him the card. "Who the fuck is doing this and why? You need to pack because we are leaving. I'm getting you to Scotland."

I'm not running; instead, I call the police, and an hour later, they arrive, "Who do you think would want to threaten you, Ms. Frost?"

"It's obviously someone who knows my first name and wants to let me know they know where I live. Who would want to send me black dahlias and why? If I knew, I wouldn't need to call the NYPD. That is why I called you. That is also why I brought you the note I received weeks ago that was delivered here in a postal mailer. I opened it to find an invitation-sized card that said I had more issues than daddy issues. Has anyone found out anything about that? I suggest you start by talking to the detective handling the stalking case."

Roland tells the police officer, "She and her stepfather have no love between them. There have been threats, but I don't think he is smart enough to pull this off. And I am sure he is too lazy to come to New York to harass her. You should be aware of it." The police leave and take the flowers and card with them.

"I don't have high hopes of the NYPD finding out who is stalking me. I took the note to the police before leaving for California and checked on the status after returning to New York. They've got no fingerprints, and the security footage only revealed verified postal workers. I mean, it's New York, and it's not a murder, so I doubt it gets high priority. I should have never done the book signings or the television appearances. Although your grand gestures were romantic, I am sure they've had an adverse effect if you consider forevermrshughes and those threats," I tell Roland after I blow my nose and wipe my eyes.

"I don't believe this has to do with me. I didn't write a book about my life. This isn't my fault. How do you know it doesn't have to do with Derek or Bob? I didn't put new names on two old abusers and expect them not to strike out."

"Oh, is that so? My real name was leaked before you made your grand entrance into my book signing and life, but my face was virtually unknown until paired with yours. I don't believe this is about my book. Bob and Derek are both about my book, but why would they feel the need to send notes and black dahlias when I've had face-to-face conflicts with them already? I am sure this has to do with you and me. You can't think those flowers were delivered here the night after our television appearance and my near trampling by mistake? Maybe if you hadn't made another grand appearance with me last night, none of this would be happening. How do we know it's not about you and your fandom?"

"So, you are angry with me because I crashed your book signing now? And surprised you last night? That's rubbish." I hear concern, but I also hear an edge in his voice, like when he thought Derek would hurt me. He looks wounded and disappears back upstairs to the office.

Made to feel uncomfortable, Charlotte prepares to leave, "He feels awful about this, Dahlia."

I look around the room, making sure Roland hasn't come back downstairs, "This wasn't his fault. It was mine. I ask to go. Look, Charlotte, the note I received, the black dahlias, and everything else has me spooked, but I don't think it is related to what happened last night. Today, I'm calling a private detective if Roland quits hovering over me long enough. I wanted him to think I was upset, so he'll give me some distance. He doesn't share my sentiment, but I believe he has a leak in his inner circle. Maybe forevermrshughes is someone who has contact with him in some aspect of his career. True, the note or flowers could be Derek or Bob, but what happened last night wasn't."

Roland races down the stairs; I place my fingers to my lips to silence Charlotte and my conversation. He sits beside me, and we change the subject. It's as good a time as any to tell Charlotte our news.

"Charlotte, sit down a second, please. Since Roland and I are both sitting here, there is something we need to tell you." She sits, and I can't help but laugh at her "WTF now?" expression.

"When we went to the emergency room last night, we found out something," I deliberately look concerned.

"What?" She rolls her eyes and wipes the sweat from her hands.

"Tell her, Roland."

He looks like a deer in the headlights. "Why me? Are you sure?" I shake my head, and Roland grabs Charlotte's hand, "Charlotte, Whisky Girl and I are going to have a baby." He smiles and looks genuinely happy at this news. We've not yet had enough time to discuss it, but his smile comforts me.

"Oh, I'm so happy for you both." Charlotte stutters her words. "I'm a bit shocked, too, I have to say. It's soon, don't you think?"

"Well, it wasn't planned, but here we are," I tell her.

"Oh, I didn't think for a second it was planned, knowing how you feel about having a child."

Roland stares at her and then back at me without speaking. The room falls awkwardly silent. Roland finally breaks the silence. "Let's change the subject until we can talk about that. I have some news. They want me to fly back to LA and do some promotion for the Bond film since I begged to release the trailer sooner than initially planned. I can tell them no if you'd prefer I stay here and you need me. I feel awful about everything, and I don't think leaving you is a good idea."

"Oh, I think I can manage just fine without you," I reply,

but he looks wounded. "I didn't mean anything by it, Roland. I'm fine. I don't need you here to watch me stay off my foot, eat fattening food, and answer fan mail. Besides, Sunday night, when the new episode of *Outlander* is released, I'll ignore you anyway. I will be safe because I'm not leaving." I laugh, and it hurts my ribs.

"I see how you are," he teases.

"Charlotte is never but a phone call away."

"She is stuck with me, Roland," Charlotte adds to the conversation.

He kisses my lips and my belly. "She's stuck with me too. Promise me you aren't leaving until I get back."

"I promise."

"I'll tell them I will fly out tomorrow. After I finish in LA, we'll return to Scotland together, right?"

Charlotte looks at me, and I nod to her and Roland. "I'm out of here. You don't need my company." Charlotte leaves with a huge smile on her face calling herself Aunt Char. Roland climbs the stairs to the office to handle business, and I google a private detective and make an appointment of my own. Then I pull the list of obstetricians from my purse and make an appointment. I lie here and look around the apartment. Not everyone has to have their environment calm and sterile, but I do. I add a touch of color here and there. Plants and flowers bring life to my apartment and depict my personality. I'm not home enough to care for a pet or give one attention. If a caregiver doesn't have the time or aptitude to show affection and shower them with attention, I question having something, whether a child or an animal, that depends on me for their love. I question what kind of mother I will be. The answer that comes back to me is scary. I am terrified at the thought. At least I have always known what I can and can't spare emotionally.

Later, thirsty, I hop to the kitchen to get a bottle of water.

Roland finds me there and scolds me for getting up. Picking me up, he sets me on the island. "I'm happy you've called the police, and I know you're scared, but I want you to know what I think. I think it is Derek Duncan. Maybe because of the novel and you hinted toward the man with white hair and having daddy issues, but maybe he thinks you will reveal more in the series. Maybe you weren't raped. Maybe it was consensual in his eyes, even if you were drunk. I don't trust the man. I don't trust he just happened upon you on the beach and picked you up as if you were a child." Roland gives me his opinion and adds, "I've not been in a relationship for years, so I am a bit out of practice, but I feel it is my responsibility to protect you."

"I appreciate that. It could be, I suppose. Roland, I called a private detective just a bit ago. The man's last name is Brummett, and he is a retired NYPD detective. He said he'll work with the NYPD and get me answers." I kiss his lips, and he pulls me into a hug.

"Good thinking. Now, tell me, since you don't want to be seen with me in public, what do you suggest we do to pass the time before I leave tomorrow? All I could think about this past month was getting you alone. That's not gone as planned." Standing between my legs, he pulls my t-shirt and bra over my head and throws them to the floor towards the living room. He releases my hair from the bun, so my hair falls around my back.

I remove his t-shirt and kiss his muscular pecs while releasing his belt, pulling it out of its loops, and throwing it onto the pile holding our shirts. I unfasten his jeans; they fall to the floor, and he steps out of them. Carefully, sliding off the counter, I stand on my left foot in front of him before I lower myself to my knees and rid him of his boxers. He stands before me naked as I grab on to the solidness of his thighs and love him.

He grips the island as I dig my fingernails into his thighs. I can hear his labored breathing and feel his body tighten as he succumbs to my talents. I feel his strong legs tremble, and it pleasures me to know I can make this man of solid rock quiver.

After assisting me to my feet, he carries and lays me on the sectional. Removing the rest of my clothing, he positions himself between my legs. He is hungry for me and brings me to climax repeatedly. My body rocks from side to side as I writhe in ecstasy before he carries me upstairs and into my bedroom. We spend our entire day in and out of bed, talking, laughing, and making plans for our trip to Scotland, refusing to think or talk about the world outside these walls.

I lie here watching him sleep and playing out how my life has changed in only seven weeks. I must've fallen asleep because the next thing I feel is the bed move; Roland is tying his trainers when I sit up. "I'm going for a run," he says. I roll over and go back to sleep. He hadn't returned when I woke. I check the time; my mind jumps back and forth between scenarios of what could've happened to him, mobs, kidnappers, alien abductions. At this point, I feel anything is possible. I've never been a social person but being anti-social and paranoid are very different things. Picking up my phone to call and check on him, I am relieved when he returns sweaty and safe. I breathe a bit easier.

Roland, showered and packed, steps onto the elevator after I plead, "Be careful. I have a bad feeling this will worsen before it gets better."

"I will," he assures me as the elevator doors close behind him.

Chapter 14

Somebody's Watching Me

March 15th

I leave my apartment no longer on crutches for the first time since the mob incident to have my initial obstetric visit. When I go, however, I not only have Charlotte waiting in the SUV for me, but I also have a bodyguard riding along with my driver. The doctor examines me and estimates I am five weeks pregnant, which tells me I got pregnant the first time we made love.

After the appointment, we instruct the driver to take us to a business office where we meet the private detective face to face. I need to personally hand him the yellow manila envelope I opened after discovering it in the fan mailbag. Out of the fifty or sixty items, I opened the day Roland left, this one eight by ten manila envelope stood out. It didn't have a return address but was mailed from New York. I reached in, expecting to pull out a letter or a photo of someone. That wouldn't be the first time someone sent me a picture to autograph and asked me to return it. Instead, the envelope holds two eight-by-ten glossy photos of Roland. One is a photo of him and me in bed in what appears to be our hotel room in Santa Monica by the bedspread and room colors. The second photo is of Roland in bed with another woman. From my brief examination of it, I can tell it's him, but I believe the image to be older because his hair is longer. I can't stand looking at the image of him and another woman. I did notice she has dark hair. Charlotte waits in the SUV while the bodyguard escorts me inside to meet Mr. Brummett, where I hand him the original photos.

"I want these returned to me personally as soon as you search for fingerprints." I'm shaking. I am completely over-whelmed and trying to get through this until Roland and I leave for Scotland. "Whoever is stalking us is here, and they are close, Mr. Brummett. They have magnified their threats, and I'm fearful for not only myself and my baby but for my mom, Roland, and Charlotte.

"No, problem, ma'am. I am flying to Los Angeles as soon as you leave the office. I will find answers for you. It sounds like the stalker knows Mr. Hughes. I can't speak about the note and flowers you received, but I have a great relationship with the police department, considering I am a retired NYPD officer myself." After shaking his hand, I turn to leave the office.

Instead, I face him, "I don't think it is all related. I think I have someone pissed at me, and I have given you a list of who those somebodies may be, and I also believe I am being targeted because of my relationship with Roland. I need answers. Find out whatever you can about Derek Duncan. He could be behind it all. I don't put anything past him, or my stepfather, for that matter."

"And you will have them, that I can guarantee. I can't guar-antee how quickly, though."

"I will be leaving the country as soon as Mr. Hughes is finished with his business here in the States. You can reach me by phone."

The Truth

Charlotte and I arrive at Sona's for lunch with no fanfare, which is enjoyable. I can't help but think about what happened to Roland and me two weeks ago and question whether I should be seen out, but my only other option is to be a prisoner in my home. I might've been okay with that at one time, but I have changed. I glance out the restaurant window and see the bodyguard standing by the SUV. I have only today learned his name is Roger. Having him nearby does make me feel safer.

After lunch, I excuse myself from the table to visit the lady's room. While washing my hands, I glance into the mirror after the door behind me opens to see the face of Derek Duncan staring back at me. Shocked, I turn my body and stand prepared to defend myself this time. He's not picking me up like a child or grabbing me this time, not without a fight. He holds the handle to the bathroom door so no one can enter. I reach into my purse and pull out my mace, placing it in my hand and preparing to squeeze the trigger. "I don't know what the hell is wrong with you, Derek. Have you lost your mind? What do you want from me?"

"I don't want to hurt you, Dahlia, for Christ's sake. All I've been trying to do is talk to you in private, which is impossible to do. After all those years, I couldn't believe it was you on the beach. I know what you told my daughter, and I lost everything over it and had to rebuild my life, which I have done, and I have no intention of losing everything again if you decide to accuse me of rape in your next book or your next twenty books. I didn't touch you. I didn't take you to that hotel, but...."

Someone pulls the handle to open the door, and Charlotte steps in when Derek lets go of it. Shocked to discover a man in the ladies' room, then to recognize Derek Duncan, she asks, "What the hell is going on? Dahlia, are you okay? Do we need to call the police?" Charlotte, cell phone in hand, prepares to push the call button to the NYPD.

169

Wide-eyed, Derek scrambles out of the bathroom. I step out quickly. "Derek," I snap, and he turns to face me, "Then who did?" He says nothing. Infuriated, I say, "If you ever come near me again, I will do whatever is within my means, which is plenty, to put you away for a very long time. Stay away from me, and don't send me any more flowers." He seems confused and opens his mouth to speak but doesn't.

"Dahlia, call the police now," Charlotte demands as a man entering the adjacent men's room snaps a photo of the scene playing out. Derek searches my face before turning to leave.

"Charlotte, he said he didn't attack me, and I wasn't about to stand here and ask him questions, but there is more to the story. He could've hurt me if he tried, but he wasn't trying. Let's go."

"That will prove to be a mistake, believe me," Charlotte pauses, then continues, "What is he doing in New York?"

"I don't know, Charlotte, but people come to New York for many reasons. He is a producer. What bothers me is how he knew I was here, or is it a coincidence? I don't believe that. Wasn't there a photo of Roland and me while we ate the other night?"

We reach the SUV, and on the way home, I scan my social media and find the photo I was talking about. I search for Derek Duncan on each platform and block him from each. We drop Charlotte off at her apartment.

Arriving home, I know I need to call Roland, but I don't know what he'll do or say. His voicemail picks up, so I leave a vague message. I think Mr. Brummett will find some answers with all the players in the LA vicinity over the next few weeks. As for me, I will now have Roger escort me to the bathroom as well.

The next morning, my quiet is interrupted. I'm not prepared to have the whirlwind, Charlotte, come into the apartment in a tizzy. "What's wrong?" I look up from my morning coffee.

"I told you that letting him walk away would prove a mistake." She throws a gossip rag magazine down in front of me. "I want to suggest that you scroll through your social media. Fans tagged Frances Slater in photos. Fans speculate that you and Roland had a fight at the hospital after your accident, verified by a nurse on duty that night. You won't like hearing this, but you need to know."

"What?"

"It's all your fault there was a breakup. The speculation is you and the man, Derek, had a fling, and Roland found out."

Standing up, talking with my hands, and stomping my non-injured foot, I face Charlotte. "You've got to be kidding me. We just went on national television and made it clear we were together, but my reputation is questioned because a photo of Derek was in my feed. Roland takes photos with women all the time," I scream. "We have not broken up. He's in California, and I'm here."

"Did you tell him about this last night?"

"Yes, I called him when I got home and left a message."

"You need to comment and squash this on social media right away. Post a photo of you and Roland. I'm sure you've taken some while he was here in the apartment. You don't have to comment; you know Roland will. He is a social media junkie. That will end all the speculation and chatter. The tabloids picked up on it; the photo of you and Derek is on the cover. Don't shoot the messenger." I turn the magazine over and see the photo that the passerby took and sold to the magazine. The headline reads, *The Halsey heiress, Dahlia Frost, caught in Sona's ladies' room with movie producer Derek Duncan. Bond, James Bond, is GONE.*

"Where is Olivia? Why hasn't she been handling what I pay

her to handle? You're doing all the jobs." Out of habit, I pour myself a dram.

"What the hell are you doing?" Charlotte asks, and I look down and smile. "It's a habit. I could use a drink right about now." I pour the whisky back into the bottle; instead, I grab my new favorite drink, a bottle of water. "Okay, where is Olivia?"

"She needed time off to go to see her mother."

"Oh, I'm sorry. I didn't know. What's wrong with her mother? So, did she have to go to London, or does her mother reside here in the states?

"I don't know, Dahlia. I didn't play 20 questions with her. She said her mother was ill."

"Okay. I'm sorry. I want to know if she plans on keeping her job and if she does, tell her to handle this now—not you. You have too many jobs as it is. Shit, keeping up with me is a full-time job. I understand if she can't be here, but hire someone else, Charlotte. You need help, and it isn't going to be me like we planned. Pour yourself a coffee. I need to call Roland." I look at the clock and see it is only 7:00 a.m. in LA. "Pour me some more, too, if you don't mind."

I open the gossip rag and read it as Charlotte calls Olivia. "Olivia, have you seen the tabloids?" There is an extended pause before Charlotte says, "Dahlia wants to know if you can handle this from your Mum's house? Great. We hope your mum feels better soon." I look to Charlotte, and she nods, "She's on it."

Thirty minutes later, my phone rings, and when I see the caller ID, I see Roland's face pop up. "Shit!" I answer, "Hey, babe." I use the sweetest voice I can because I know what is coming.

"Now what? Please tell me you weren't talking to him." His voice raised, "Where were you?"

"I left a voice mail telling you what happened. Charlotte was standing right there."

"I can see that. I'm holding the rag in my hand. It was brought to me with my morning coffee. Apparently, James Bond can't handle his woman." He makes a grunting noise.

"Look, I can't help what some passerby sold to the magazine any more than I can help that Derek followed me into the bathroom to pee."

"No, but if the cops had him on the ground putting cuffs on him, I guarantee the headlines would look different." He is furious and tells me he is flying back to New York immediately.

"You need to take care of business so we can get to Scotland sooner than later."

"I'm finished here, and I am flying there so we can fly out of LaGuardia together in a highly visible fashion. I'll be there in a few days. Can you be ready to go by then?"

"I'll be ready."

"I love you, Whisky Girl. Stay put, stay safe, and for God's sake, stay out of trouble."

"I haven't done anything, Roland," I said as he hung up.

Now briefed with the updated plans, Charlotte seems happier that I will be flying with Roland. "What about the rest of your book signings here in the States?"

"How many do I have scheduled? I didn't think there were but a couple since we didn't know how soon the mask mandates would lift or how much traveling I could do when we booked them last year."

"I can postpone them using the excuse of the pregnancy and wanting to wait until after the baby's birth."

"I don't want the news of my pregnancy to be public knowledge. Do whatever you need to do without releasing that info, please. Everyone knows I got hurt in the incident so maybe use that." When did I become an invalid? Oh, I know, the minute

173

Roland's fame infected my life. I hate this, but I remind myself it is all for our child's safety. Charlotte leaves promising to hold the fort down at the publishing company, my apartment, and keeping on Olivia to handle the media.

Calling Mr. Brummett, "I know you probably don't have anything for me yet, but where are the photos? I need to take them with me before I leave the country. I need to show my boyfriend."

"They are in the custody of my friend, Sergeant Voight. Call him, and he'll get them to you. He has finished with them. I was planning to call you. They found a partial print on the photo of Mr. Hughes and the other woman but don't have a hit yet."

"Good. I'll call him today. Roland is leaving LA in two days so we can fly to Scotland. Whatever the cost, I need answers no matter where the leads take you, Mr. Brummett. It's been two months since I received the first note and still nothing from the police. I had an incident here yesterday."

"Yes, ma'am, news travels fast, and magazines are every-where. I have a copy lying here in the front seat of the car. I'm heading to the airport soon to check out Derek Duncan. He's on a flight back to LA now; don't worry; I will track his flights from now on, too. I got this. Don't concern yourself with reaching out to Voight; I'll call him and tell him to drop the photos off to you ASAP."

"Thanks, Mr. Brummett. I appreciate that."

I disconnect and immediately call Mom. She answers, "Hello."

"How are you?"

"I'm doing great. How are you, Dahlia?"

I spend the next 45 minutes filling Mom in on some of the things happening. She doesn't need to know everything. "I have good news for you, though." I wait.

"What is that?"

"It looks like I'll be giving you a grandchild after all."

"Dahlia, I am so happy. Are you happy, sweetie?" she screams out of excitement.

"I think so. I'm trying to be, but it has been one thing after another, and now I have to worry about your safety, Roland's, and the baby's."

"And your own, Dahlia. Don't forget about taking care of yourself."

"I won't, Mom, but please keep your head down and eyes open just in case."

"Oh, I've already been contacted to comment on the 'Halsey heiress' and if I would like to comment about your novel, *Daddy Issues*. I hadn't heard about you getting knocked down and almost trampled. When did that happen?"

"March third. Did you watch the Jimmy Fallon episode with me and the surprise guest, James Bond, a.k.a Roland Hughes?"

"No. How wonderful is that, though? I'm so proud of both of you. I will stream it all tonight to keep up with you two. Dahlia, you go to Scotland and watch out for your family. I am fine, and if I need anything, I will let you know. I'm happy, and my new meds are working, so I'm the least of your worries. I love you."

"Nice to hear, Mom. I love you, too. I'll keep in touch."

Chapter 15

Unless It's With You

March 30th

The driver arrives at the apartment, and I ask Roland to go down ahead of me. I'm kneeling over the toilet yet again this morning. Morning sickness or nerves, the reason for it doesn't matter because it's become a daily occurrence. I'm unsure if I am frazzled because I'm running behind on a day that includes a seven-hour flight with Roland or, worse, having to walk through the airport with him. He has been anxious to return to Scotland since arriving in New York, but I haven't felt well enough. But today is the day regardless of how I feel. I stop and glance out the floor-to-ceiling windows overlooking Central Park, knowing I will miss my home. I stand in the foyer and glance around one more time before stepping into the elevator. I don't know if I'll be back before the baby is born, and that is a long time to be away from my home. I've never lived anywhere longer or felt more secure than here. I push the main floor lobby button.

The elevator chimes. I look across the marble floor and watch the doorman holding the door open as I approach him and step out on the sidewalk just as my luggage is loaded. Roland is signing autographs and taking photos. I smile and wave as I'm escorted to the SUV; I don't care to autograph anything else again. Roland turns me around before I step into the vehicle and wraps his arm over my shoulder as pictures are taken. I smile, and I'm not surprised there is no mention of a certain producer, at least not to Roland.

We meet the paparazzi as we arrive at the airport as well. Roland charms the crowd in his usual way while keeping me close to him and the bodyguard surrounding us.

I grabbed a gossip rag while in the airport containing a retraction article. Olivia submitted a statement from Derek Duncan denying it was him in the photo, which is easily done since it's the back of an older man's head. That white hair could belong to anyone. It reads that they are sorry they reported in error. Roland Hughes and Dahlia Frost have not broken up. The older man in the photo caught Dahlia Frost exiting the lady's room of a prominent New York restaurant and was merely asking for an autograph.

I hand the magazine to Roland, and he grins as he reads the article. He scrolls through his calendar and shows me how full his appearance schedule is. "Tell me, love where are we fitting in the birth of our child into this schedule?" he jokes. I point to November and advise him to reschedule what is there, especially if he is supposed to be in another country than I am.

When we arrive at Roland's house, it is after dark. Our luggage is placed inside the door, and then we are alone. I don't have much time to familiarize myself with his house and the city before he leaves again. He turns on a replay of a recently missed rugby match, and I fall asleep with my head in his lap again. I wake up when he asks if I'm ready for bed.

"Well, of course, I was already asleep." I can sit down and doze off without realizing it. Climbing into bed, I find my favorite position, cuddle up next to him, resting my head on his arm as he presses his lips to mine. He gently trails to my ears and neck, lingering over each spot his lips touch, sending shivers through my body. He hovers his body over mine; as I reach up and hold his face in my hands, filling me with so much love, I think I'll burst. I stare into his eyes, and in a moment of passion, I whisper, "I lo—" but I stop myself. If I speak the words, it will fade away; it will be gone. Tonight, we make love, body, and soul.

"I love that our child is growing inside your belly. The baby is due in October, aye?" he asks as I am nested into him, and his arm rests across my waist.

"Yes, October 31st to November 4th is my guess."

"Seven months to prepare. That is not much time."

"No, it isn't. Are you nervous? I am, and not just about the baby."

"I am too. We won't be an ocean apart, though. I promise you and the baby will be safe." We discuss the need for a bodyguard while I live here. Before hiring a bodyguard, I want to see how things go, but I agree to have a driver.

"All the threats in the US were extreme, and I'm concerned about what will happen when people know about the pregnancy. We can't hide it forever. Have you paid attention to this belly? You can't promise that Roland, although being here in Scotland feels safer."

"Yes, love, I am holding this belly and our baby in my hand. I know."

I wake to the sunlight streaming in the big windows, and rays of sunbeams drape across a room I am unfamiliar with. I lay still, glancing across the room decorated in simple masculine décor. I am grateful there aren't whiskey posters, rugby posters, or huge photos of himself on the wall. He has sophisticated taste. When I recall I am waking up in Scotland and Roland's bed, I flip over and watch him sleep before I touch his shoulder gently with my lips and leave the bedroom quietly, closing the door behind me.

I find my way to the kitchen and, more importantly, the espresso maker. I wander around the meticulous house with my cup of coffee. I can't help but wince at the thought of us with a child, two single, meticulous people in our late thirties. I guess we'll learn to love messy. I grab a blanket for my lap and sit on the deck, realizing I slept better last night than I have slept in a very long time. I don't know how much time passes as I read my book and enjoy the peace and sense of safety before the sound of something breaking startles me. Standing inside the house, I watch Roland move from spot to spot, cleaning up whatever the glass on the floor used to be. He seems tense. "Is everything all right, Roland?"

"Yes, Dahlia, everything is fine," he replies sharply. "Did I kick you in my sleep or move something you didn't want to be moved?" I ask softly, only slightly teasing since he hardly ever calls me Dahlia. He takes his coffee to the island and sits down. I follow. He reaches over and holds my hand briefly, "I am fine. Jet lag, maybe. How are you this morning?"

"I feel great. No nausea yet."

"Good," Roland places the mail in front of him and notices a package. He opens the mail, slides the box in front of him, cuts the packaging tape, and looks inside the box. He shuts the box, sits back down, and drinks his coffee. Then he looks at me. "How many people know you are pregnant?"

"Me, you, Charlotte, and my mom. Why?"

"I don't want to upset you, but someone else knows. That makes a total of five people. What about the doctor in the ER and the obstetrician?"

"Yes, but that info is confidential."

He pushes the box over in front of me. I don't understand

what is happening, but I sense a heaviness. There is nothing
dark about this house, but it's suffocating here at this exact
minute. I peek inside the box and pull out a blue-baby blanket, a
pink baby blanket, a dummy, a romper, and booties in a basket.
At the bottom of the box, there is a note. "There is a note,
Roland." I pull the note out, but Roland takes it from me to read
it first.

He reads it aloud, "Congratulations on your upcoming
offspring."

He pulls me into his arms, and I feel his concern, "What
else does it say?"

"Nothing."

"Did you tell anyone? Maybe someone sent these to you as a
gift. It doesn't feel threatening."

Roland looks at the box, which doesn't have a return address
or postage.

"Nothing is confidential where you and I are concerned," he
sighs before continuing, "Maybe you're right. I told my mum.
She's the fifth person that knows, but I don't see her bringing me
a box of baby items like this. But that doesn't explain the broken
mirror."

"What broken mirror?" He pulls me into the bedroom and
closes the door. I recognize the mirror from years ago. It's the
same one he had in his flat in London where I wrote him the
message, "No matter the distance, I am right here with you," in
bright red lipstick across the glass before I left to return to the
US. "Oh, no, what happened to it? I can't believe you still have
it." It's not broken on the floor but shattered into a kaleidoscope
of broken pieces within its frame. I assume it took a direct hit
dead center with something. I see nothing that could've caused
this. Roland removes the mirror, carries it to the kitchen island,
and lays it flat. While he is distraught over what this may or may
not be, I feel it's best not to keep my news to myself any longer. I

180

need to show him the photos. I hate to, but he'll have more answers than I do about who is in the picture with him. I retrieve the large yellow envelope from my suitcase and sit on the couch. He sits down beside me, and I hand it to him. "This is a threat."

"What is this, and where did you get them?" He scoots up on the edge of his couch seat and leans forward while looking down at them. While running his fingers through his wavy blond hair, his face shows little reaction to the photos, but the tone of his voice and his gestures are transparent. He recognizes the woman in the second photo.

"I discovered these the day you flew back to California, in the bag of fan mail Charlotte had brought over."

"I know better than to ask because I know the answer. Did you call the police?" Roland asks.

"No, but I did take them to the private detective I told you I hired, and he is working with a detective on the force. They found a partial fingerprint on the photo of you and the other woman, but they hadn't got any hits on it last I checked."

"I'm happy you've hired someone who makes all this a priority. I don't know what else we can do. This photo of me with another woman had to be years ago. You can't even see either of the faces in the photo. I'm not sure if it's even me. I can't even tell who it is or where I was." He slams the photo and his fist down on the table. I jump. "I'm sorry. I'm tired of this."

"Don't be sorry. We weren't together, were we? But it is you. I can tell that body anywhere." I touch his abs and run my hands down to his thighs. Then I twist my body to face him and fold my legs under me. "This is strange and disturbing. How did someone get a picture of us making love in the hotel while we were in California? It couldn't be from outside the window. That means it was through a camera placed in our room. Someone took a photo of you many years ago, which means our stalker is your stalker. It's someone who has been following you a long time. It's not about the book. It's someone who knows you or wants to know you. I think it's someone who wants to be forevermrshughes in real life. She's close to us, and she's getting desperate. Why else would we be bombarded with an arsenal of threats in the past few weeks."

Roland stares at the photos for a bit. "Aye. Maybe you're right. I could've sworn this had to do with the book but maybe it is about you and me. It's hard to know how far this goes back by the old photo; I bet they were at your signing in London and California."

"Every time we are photographed together or seen in public, we receive a threat. I'm not being nosey, but who is the woman in the photo?"

"Oh shit, I don't know."

"Seriously, that many, huh?"

"No, I could tell you the name of every woman I've ever slept with, but I can't place the year or place in this photo."

I take the photo from him and look closely, but just like the first time I saw them, I feel like a peeping Tom. "What I know for sure is that she has dark hair. It could be forevermrshughes and the one sending the threatening items."

"Aye. Let me think about it. I'm going for a run. I'd ask you to go, but I'm running until I get this mess out of my head, and I think you need to have a bodyguard here, just to be safe. And I'm going to call the police. I want to call the security company and have the security video checked. Someone was in the house. While I'm running, get dressed; we're leaving for the day." He runs out the door.

As I enter the living room, he returns home from his run an hour later. He informs me he is on the phone with the authorities and the security company. "As soon as they arrive, we are leaving. You might want to dress warmer. I want to take the Harley out. I'm getting in the shower."

"Okay."

Roland has the bike out thirty minutes later as the security team arrives. He takes them inside and returns with one of the men, "I want it checked, and I want more cameras and alarms, whatever it needs. Then I want the other house checked top to bottom. Call me after you've completed looking through the footage, please." Roland climbs on the bike, and I climb on after him, then we leave for an entire day of sightseeing. Feeling nearly invisible, we travel through Glasgow, visiting the Kelpies, Falkirk Wheel, and the Botanic Gardens, and stopping to eat. Hours later, his phone rings, and he takes us back to the house.

That night, while lying in bed, he informs me there is no physical evidence, other than the broken mirror and a package magically appearing, of anyone in the house other than the housekeeper, Mrs. McCann, whom I will meet Monday when she returns to work. The video shows her carrying the mail in but not a package. They are contacting the maintenance man and gardener as well. There isn't a camera in the bedroom, so he has no idea what happened to the mirror. He said there were two times that the cameras weren't recording.

* * *

It's been nearly a month since we arrived at Roland's home and were greeted with the baby item box. Still, there has been no word from anyone concerning the notes, flowers, photos, or baby item box, but we've not had any threats or concerns since. Roland, staying on the side of caution, especially since he's been out of the country, has a bodyguard and driver to take me where I need to go, which today is a quick trip to my new obstetrician.

I don't expect him to be back in town or home when the driver drops me off, but Roland opens the door before I reach for the handle. He pulls me into a tight hug, and I hug him even tighter. Then the smell of food punches me in the gut. I glance around and see the dining room table set beautifully. It touches my heart but turns my stomach, and I make a straight line for the master bathroom. Dampening a washcloth with cold water—morning sickness, my ass, I place it on the back of my neck. I will be in my second trimester in a matter of days, and instead of the sickness slowing, it seems to have increased to all-day and all-night sickness. Outside the four walls of this room, Roland prepares something in the kitchen that my nauseated stomach does not want, but I want to appreciate his efforts. I brush my teeth, smile, and try it again. "I should be over this sickness by now. I am so sorry," I say as I reach the table. "Did you do all this yourself? You've gone to so much trouble."

"No, I had Ms. McCann do it, but I could if I'd had time."

"How wonderful. I'm starving, but I can't guarantee I can eat anything."

Roland pulls the chair out for me and then takes his seat. He pours two glasses of champagne, and I know better than attempt it, so I sip my water. We've not had much time to talk in the last month, a text or a call every couple of days due to his hectic schedule. He enthusiastically shares all he has accomplished for the charity event, his film schedules, and his new book. I am thrilled for him.

On the other hand, I hardly recognize the woman I've become. The only things on my agenda are relaxing and enjoying my new life in Scotland. I lift my glass, "Cheers to all your success," I toast. He raises his glass, and as they clink, I notice something move inside my flute. A closer look shows a solitary diamond ring sparkling at me. "What have you done?" I let out a quiet squeal of delight as I forget nausea and focus on my sheer joy and happiness.

"Drink up."

"You drink up. I can't." He empties my glass with one gulp and turns the ring out. He pats it dry. My heart is pounding as he steps in front of me and bends on one knee. My head screams for him to get up because he doesn't know what he is doing. Marriage? A baby? My mind is racing, but as surprised as I am by his proposal, I am also blanketed with a peace I've never known. His calm spirit quiets the crazies inside of me. I move the ruby and diamond ring I've had for as long as I can remember to my right hand.

He places my left hand in his and grins, "Whisky Girl, I dare ya to marry me." I recognize his words when he dared me to face my fear of the smell of whiskey. I smile, recalling how that one dare changed my life. If I had not gotten over my fear, he and I could've never been a couple. If I want this life, I must let go of the fear of failing him. He knows the words he just asked me are the perfect combination.

I stare at him for what feels like hours but is only actually seconds, "I'll take that dare." I hope he knows what he is doing and asking me to do.

"Forever is a long time."

"I can do forever with you, Roland. I promise." I smile as it occurs to me that he and I deserve each other and everything that goes with it. I will one day need to remind him how much he wanted me and his grand gestures.

"Are you sure that you can?"

"Yes."

He stands and pulls me up to him. Being in his arms is where I belong. "I was going to wait until we could fly off to some romantic place, but I didn't want to wait another day. I promise I'll fly you anywhere you want for our honeymoon, and I'll propose again."

"This is the perfect place and time while I'm pregnant and

nauseous. That means you love me even at my worst. Roland, you deserve so much better than me."

"Shush. I deserve you and all that comes with it."

As he holds me in his arms, I tip my head to look into his eyes, "I'll remind you of that often." I step back while holding his hands, "I can't say I knew patience when I was young, but I learned to be patient. I learned to pray. I also learned two forces are listening when we pray, so I learned to be careful what I pray for. I prayed for you to find me. Then, I asked God not to let you find me if you couldn't love me and the scars I carry under my clothes. Next thing I knew, I was on a plane to London."

* * *

Fifteen weeks ago, I stood in the bathroom of the Shangri-La at the Shard, and I was a completely different woman. I wasn't involved with a man, let alone engaged to Roland, and I wasn't pregnant with his child. Then again, I wasn't being stalked, my mother still lived with her husband, and the list continues. This morning, I shake my head, place my hands on the counter, focus on the newly placed three-carat-sized princess cut diamond, and lean forward. My long hair is dripping water all over the floor of Roland's bathroom. I'm happy, and I'm not sure I have the right to be. Our joy has cost someone something, or we wouldn't have been harassed and stalked, and I'm finding it difficult to relax and move past it. I turn sideways and place protective hands over my ever-rounder belly.

Today is Roland's birthday, and tonight is the annual charity event he attends. I set the entire day aside to get ready while he is in and out of the house doing whatever he needs to do. Toward the afternoon, I wander around the property looking for him. Next, I search the garage; his vehicles are here, so he's not left. Searching inside the house, I go upstairs to his gym, but he isn't there. Finally, I hear music and stand out of sight while listening to him play guitar. He is really good, but when he sees me, he stops. "I didn't know you could play. You are really good."

"Thank you. I play when I want to relax and usually only when I am home, which isn't often, as you know."

"Are you okay? Are you nervous about something other than our normal?"

"Not really, but I am always on guard anymore. Tonight should be a nice change. I love it. You will, too."

"I think so, too. I was looking for you because I have something to give you for your birthday." I hand him a small box. He pulls out a silver band engraved with the words, I-promise-forever. I watch as he turns the ring to read the inscription. "It's for your right ring finger, Roland."

"Thank you, love. Forever and always, right?" He takes the ring out of the box and puts it on his right-handed ring finger. I smile and glimpse what it will look like doing forever with him.

Hours later, when we arrive at the convention center, the driver opens the door to the SUV. I step out first in a silky silver-colored gown that gathers under my breast and hides my baby bump. I'm overcome with emotion when I watch Roland step out. I watch him as his muscular calves are hidden in his black boots and kilt socks. His bare knees peek out below his kilt. He stands, and I watch him push the silver buttons through the buttonholes to secure the fitted tux jacket, defining his muscular chest and arms. His dark-blue kilt stops just above his knees, his sporran hanging seductively from his hips.

The full effect sweeps over me, and I turn away to push the air out of my lungs that I had been holding, then fan my face. How did I get so lucky? He leads me, and I love it. We spend the evening with a few thousand supporters of the same charities Roland supports. I stay in the background as he does what he does best, charms the room and gets adored. I watch him intently all evening, no matter where I am, while standing in the same room and compare our gestures, his ease with people, and my caution. His trusting and open nature is evident in his open arms while I hug my elbows to protect myself and the baby growing inside me. Catching Roland searching for me in the room, I remain still and allow him to find me. I watch his smile widen from across the room. He stands to give a speech, and afterward, he seeks me out, reaches for my hand, and lays his other on my belly. I can't help but wonder if forevermrshughes is standing near him right now or staring at me as I think of her. I shake my head at the thought. The night is a spectacular event, and I'm proud to be a part of it, watching his light mood and whiskey-fueled ease as he mingles and jokes.

I am excited to get home and remove him from his kilt, just like I fantasized about since I watched him put it on this afternoon. The effects of what Roland drank tonight are apparent; he is playful and isn't ready for the party to end when we get home, so we help each other out of our clothes. He unzips the back of my silk gown, allowing it to fall to the floor with ease. Standing in front of him in my lacy bra, underwear, and thigh-high hose, he slides his arms around my waist, I pull into him, but I realize it is to help him keep his balance. He sits on the side of the bed; I slide his tux jacket off, undo his tie, remove his crisp white shirt, and run my hands through his bare chest hair. Kneeling before him, I unlace his boots to remove them when he falls backward on the bed. "Roland, are you awake? Are you all right?" When he doesn't reply, I stand and look down on him only to discover he has passed out. I finish removing his boots and sporran but leave him dressed in the one thing I wanted to get him out of, his kilt. He's too heavy to try to wrestle that off him. I cover his torso and wrap a blanket around his legs and feet. I undress, climb into bed, and put my head at the foot of the bed, next to his, then throw a blanket over myself, kiss his cheek, close my eyes, and thank God for my life.

In the morning, I open my eyes to Roland's face smiling into mine, both of us at the wrong end of the bed, and I giggle. I am immediately grateful to wake up beside him and pray that there is never another morning we wake up in different beds, houses, or countries. I watch him sleep. To think we only reunited three and one-half months ago and look at how far we've come. Roland crawls under the covers, placing his cold feet on my warm body.

"What the hell, Roland?" I squeal. He giggles. I move into the fold of his body and place my arm over his waist as he moves just enough to pull me in closer. I can't get close enough. I had forgotten what it feels like to love someone so completely that his nearness makes my heart beat faster and smothers me in emotion. I roll over and can see, touch, smell, and kiss him whenever I want. It's a dream come true. I smack myself in the forehead to make sure I'm not dreaming. "Ouch. I'm not."

"What are you doing, love? Did I just see you smack your-self?" he whispers.

I refuse to answer because I don't want him to think I have lost my mind completely. I don't want to admit how crazy I am, crazy in love with him. It's Sunday morning, and it has been an eventful weekend filled with every minute having something to be accomplished attached to it. We lay in bed longer than usual until he has the idea to get up, get dressed, and take the motor-bike for a spin around the city as we stop for coffees and pastries —the best part of being pregnant. I eat without guilt, and since I'm not drinking, I need at least one bad habit aside from Roland, and he is a habit I will never break. Roland reaches back, places his left hand on my calf, and squeezes, "Hang on." He speeds up and weaves in and out of traffic. I would be nervous if it were anyone but him driving, but I see him checking his mirrors. I look over my shoulder to see a blue four-door sedan follow us. He speeds up and weaves in and out of vehicles to lose the car. He yells, "We're going to take a longer ride. All right with you?"

"Of course." I rest my head on his shoulder, desperately wanting us to be invisible.

"What was that about?" I ask him after arriving home.

"Nothing. That happens occasionally. It's not a big deal." He kisses my cheek.

I have so much to do to prepare for our wedding only two weeks away. We agreed not to stretch out a long engagement and keep our wedding small and intimate; privacy and security are our primary concerns. Roland's mother, Jane, is going dress shopping with me and helping with the details. My mother is sorry, but she cannot attend. I sighed when I received her RSVP with that response, but I expected it. She is doing fine and loves her new live-in caregiver, and she declines our offer to fly here for the wedding or to live with us. She is afraid to fly, and she isn't fooling me.

Adjusting to my new schedule, filled with wedding and baby things, I endure several hours of boredom while scanning social media, paying particular attention to any comments that show a cause to worry, not just for myself but for Roland and our child. We haven't received any threatening notes, cards, flowers, or packages lately, so we take that as a good sign. I'm hoping that is a good thing. I set up new social media accounts in my real name. Roland and I agree that I will keep my last name instead of taking his. After the party, articles, interviews, and photos confirm our engagement and pregnancy, and the comments aren't as awful as I expected, especially since there are none from forevermrshughes. Just like he predicted, the frenzy has died down. Once the defamation trial began of a different big movie star and his ex-wife, the news media and social media seemed to have forgotten about us. Hallelujah.

I need to complete my second book, but I won't be publishing it until I have answers to the threats and stalking. Olivia has handled all publicity requests and denied them all. I am looking at colors and planning a nursery, which has proven difficult considering we don't know the sex of our child, but I do think I have decided to use the tartan Roland designed and do it in that theme—maybe. As of late, I hardly believe the reflection of my life and how it has changed.

I shouldn't allow this false sense of security, but I do. Mr. Brummett last said the only lead, the partial fingerprint, has not provided additional information. Everyone believes all clues lead to forevermrshughes stalking us and has nothing to do with the book, making me not worry about my mom. Maybe my face-to-face run-ins with Derek and Bob have settled their grievances with me. I still think forevermrshughes is close to us and doesn't ever go too far away.

I wake up, get ready, and meet Roland in the kitchen for coffee. I am picking up my wedding dress today, May 9th, only five days before our wedding, and I argue that I miss driving and neither Jane nor I need a bodyguard to tag along. Roland reluctantly agrees to let me drive his Audi to meet Jane at the bridal boutique.

Chapter 16

Secrets

May 10th

T he sound is muffled due to the rain and thunder; it's a car engine, and a door shuts. I listen and let out the breath I didn't know I was holding as the noise becomes intrusive over the background of calming rain. A door squeaks open, and suddenly my ears are assaulted with heavy stomps, softer steps, and a woman yelling. "Where is she? I can't believe you left her alone and drove to my home. What have you done to her?"

"I told ye I put her in the hole and locked her in. If ye didn't want her alone, you should've stayed with her," a solid Scottish Highland accent barks.

"What hole? Get her out now."

That sounds like Olivia's voice. Why would she do this to me?

"Ye not said anything good about this woman for the four-year ye kens her, but ye want me to be kind?"

The door opens, and the light blinds me. After my eyes slightly adjust, I see the blurred face of the faceless man from my walk. Everything about him is huge. He must be 6'3" and, I'm guessing, 300 pounds. He straddles the doorway, bends over as he reaches for me with his large hands, lifts me from the darkness, and stands me back on my feet. Then, I see Olivia standing off to the side, and she offers her hand. I refuse it and smack it away. I push the huge man as hard as possible, but he doesn't budge. He laughs at me.

"You're a piece of shit," I try to bark at him in my rough, dry voice. I've cried so much that my nose is stuffed up, and if that isn't bad enough, I can hardly see because my eyes are swollen, not to mention the dried blood and headache from the cut on my forehead.

Olivia leads me from the closet to a chair beside a hearth. The huge man puts wood in the hearth and builds a fire. "I'm no cleaning piss," he states as his back is turned to me. He doesn't look at me, but I bet he can feel the daggers my eyes are throwing. The fire quickly provides warmth to my shaking hands and legs.

"I'm not going to restrain you because if you are stupid enough to run from here and take on this rough terrain in the middle of nowhere, in the pouring down rain, you will deserve that death. I have no intention of hurting you, but I need your attention, and the only way I can have your complete, totally self-absorbed, and privileged attention is to go to this extreme. Do you understand me? His locking you in a closet, or hole as he calls it, was not in my plan, and I didn't know he did until two hours ago. I am sorry for that, Dahlia." Olivia bends over me to look at the cut on my forehead. "I'm sorry for this as well." I move my head slowly in an up and down movement. I've been shivering since I woke in the darkness. The heat coming from the small fire feels fantastic as it warms my limbs. It is May, yet it is chilly where we are. I assume we are in the highlands.

"Get out." She points at the door, "Don't come back until

the morning. See if you can follow all the instructions without hurting anyone," her anger is directed at the huge man.

"I don't want to drive to ye house. I'm tired." I understood his accent this time.

"I need to tend to the wound on her head where she fell forward and cracked her forehead. You said it was a bump; it's more than a bump. I don't care what you want. I told you not to touch her, so I can't trust you. All you had to do was sit with her, not put her in a locked closet. Do you want the money?" The man nods his head yes.

"Aye, what if she runs?"

"She won't, but if she does, I will handle it without locking her into whatever that is and scaring her to death. Look at her, you berk. I don't want her hurt." Olivia steps into the small kitchen. "I want her to listen, and I want the money. After completing the task tomorrow, bring the things on this list. Go home." I watch her follow the man outside. I hurry to remove the watch and put it in my pocket before it is spotted. I'm relieved to see this old cabin has electricity and lights. The floors are flat stone. The ceiling in the cabin's center has exposed beams no taller than seven feet. The huge man's head almost touches the top. It has three rooms: a makeshift-looking kitchen, the main room, a bedroom, and a closet. My senses are heightened; I smell wood burning in the fireplace, the sound of the wood crackling and popping under intense heat, and the darkness I see outside the window is dark, but thanks to the moon, it is not nearly as dark and black as the closet. My heart is pounding in my head. The car engine starts, and the big man leaves. Good riddance.

When Olivia walks back through the doorway with a bag in her hand, she pulls clean clothing, linens, and clean blankets from it and motions for me to follow her to an adjoining room. "You will sleep in here. I have plenty of covers to put on the bed for you. I know the cabin doesn't look like much, but there is a water closet, so you are in luck. I understand pregnant women pee a lot. I'm sorry, Dahlia." She hands me clean clothes, two bottles of water, and a washcloth. I follow her into the room. I open and guzzle the first and half of the second bottle of water before I carefully remove the watch from my pocket and hide it under the mattress. I strip off my dirty clothes, changing into the warm clothing she brought for me. My hands are still shaking as I put my jacket back on. Attempting to zip the zipper, I notice my fragmented fingernails and shiver.

Olivia begins cleaning up the puddle of piss pooled outside the closet. I think of apologizing but instantly change my mind. If I say anything to her, it will be something like "Fuck you," but I don't say that either.

I sit as still as possible and close my mouth tightly to keep my teeth from chattering. Olivia cleans and butterfly strips the cut on my forehead. "This needs stitches. I'm sorry, but it will probably scar."

"Add," I attempt to reply but my throat is still dry and rough. I finish the second bottle of water, then attempt to speak again, "Add it to the scars no one sees."

With the big man gone, and when she turns to walk away, I grab her arm, swing her around at the same time, pull myself up, clench my fist, and swing. Catching her in the face, I bloody her nose. I stand prepared as she recoils from the punch. Stepping back, Olivia wipes her face and smears blood across it.

"I'll give you that one. I'm not having an argy-bargy with a pregnant woman, and I had that coming." She walks off and sits down with a tissue in her nose and two cups of hot tea. She stokes the fire and sits down.

"Olivia, will you tell me what I'm doing here? And where is the child?" Punching her helped my nerves and my shakes. I pick up my tea and glare over the edge of my cup at her bloodied and tissue-stuffed nose. "Does my fiancé know where I am?"

"Yes. As soon as you calm down, we'll chat. You have a nice right hook, Dahlia." She touches her nose as if questioning if it is broken. I hope it is. She continues, "I can't say I've ever been hit or hit anyone before. You shouldn't get this upset while you're pregnant. Your baby senses that."

"Lucky you. I've been hit plenty. I supposed you shouldn't have abducted me or let your large friend manhandle me."

"I suppose so. He paid a young man to run to the side of your car. You shouldn't be such a selfish woman, and I wouldn't have had to go to this extreme. I will fill you in a little bit tonight, so you will at least be able to sleep, but I'll tell you everything tomorrow. We left a note in Roland's car. We told him we have you and will contact him with our ransom demands." I watch as a smile crosses her face. She is pleased with herself and enjoying this power, but I don't understand why.

"How did you know which car was his? How did you know where I was?"

"One, I'm not stupid. Two, I watched you get in and out of it. You will be amazed how your life and mine are intertwined, sister."

"Sister?"

"Yes, we are half-sisters, Dahlia. What do you think of that?"

"I don't understand. How and who?" I'm not shocked because she's not the first supposed long-lost family member to show up after my inheritance was revealed, but I'm confused.

"That will come tomorrow, I promise. But you can rest knowing I have no intention of hurting you. You are the only family I have left. I will have what I want and what my mother should've had before she died."

196

That rules out my mother from having another child I didn't know about.

Olivia continues, "She could've had a better life and enjoyed some things before she died if she had only a portion of the money you received. We'll talk tomorrow. Go to bed, and again let me remind you that if you think you can sneak out and make it anywhere on your own, you can't. I don't care what training you had and might still remember. You can't. Try to sleep."

I watch as she closes the door to the closet that held me captive. I do as I'm told and lie down on the bed, fully dressed, thankful she left the door open to warm the room. I know I should be scared, but I'm not. I foolishly believe the worse of it is probably over since the huge man isn't here. I'm worried about Roland and what he must be going through. People will show up at the house in the next day or two for wedding preparations. It occurs to me that I'm not supposed to know how long I've been here or what day it is. "Olivia," I call her name loudly.

"What, Dahlia? I'm not answering questions tonight."

"Just one, please. Does this have anything to do with my wedding, or is it coincidental you kidnapped me days before?"

Standing at the bedroom door, she leans against it with her arms folded. "Dahlia, this has to do with many things you would've known if you didn't have your head shoved so far up your arse. You felt sorry for yourself, and you are not the only victim. I'm here to tell you that many others have it worse than you could ever imagine. Now go to sleep."

I can't sleep, but like before, the sounds of the hard rain and thunder soothe the noise in my head. I have many questions but assume she has to be Dahmon's daughter, which explains what she meant by money, my inheritance. I was not the only heir. I quietly get up as daylight breaks, then glance out the window.

The green landscape goes on forever, with mountains peeking out from a sea of fog. We are at some elevation.

Entering the warm room, Olivia is awake, sitting in the chair by the hearth. "I won't ask if you slept because I know you didn't. Would you like something to drink or eat?"

"I'd love coffee or tea. I'm not hungry, but I know I need to eat; I'm guessing it's been days. How long have I been here, and what day is it?"

She brings me a coffee just the way I like it and a breakfast sandwich; she's gotten me coffee many times. She sits across from me, leans forward, puts her forearms on her knees, and glances at the cell phone in her left hand. "It is 5 a.m. May eleventh. He took you thirty-nine hours ago. After you eat, I'm going to tell you a story. I read your story in *Daddy Issues*, but I'm not exactly sure what was made up, so I have some questions for you too."

"Okay. Will you tell me why you're doing this first and what you stand to gain other than money? I picked up on that last night. What do you want me to lose?"

"No, you're the storyteller. You'll figure it out."

"Fair enough." I have no choice in the matter.

"Has anyone ever told you, Dahlia, that you are too accommodating? That is why you've been misled, lied to, and deceived. If you get mad, enraged, or sit passively and take what has been done to you, you can't save them."

"Save who?" The look she gives tells me to sit quietly. This is a first for me. I've never once been told I was accommodating.

"I should've written my own book, but I never felt the need to tell my story as you did. When I first read *Daddy Issues*, I questioned whom you wrote it for. Was it to tell about your mum and her choices? Was it to tell what a despicable man your stepfather is? Was it to tell the mental breakdown you went through after the hypnosis? Was it to get Roland to read it and find you so he would come in and sweep you off your feet? Was it to tell your story so that it would seem real? My guess is it was all of that. You needed to prove that you were not the failure you let yourself become. I get it. You wanted to punish your mum for keeping secrets from you that affected your entire life. It doesn't matter why you wrote it. What matters is that you should've done your research."

"I did my research," I inform her as she stomps away from me. While she moves about the cabin, I sit still and think about what she said. I know I did my research. I got it straight from my mother. As soon as I had the thought, hundreds of red flags started waving in my head.

Back into the living area, she sits down in the chair opposite me, bends at her waist, leans her elbows on her knees, and glares into my eyes, "No. Because if you had, then you would've known your mum lied to you. You would know that there was so much more to the story." I prepare to speak again. "If you talk again, I will stop, and we'll continue tomorrow." I shake my head in acknowledgment.

"You have no memory of the car accident or anything before your sixth birthday. That is what you wrote. When finished with this part of the story, I want you to think about your first memory. The novel reads that your father kidnapped you, right? You were missing for days, but then the police spotted his car, and he gave them chase, eventually hydroplaning into the lake. Dahmon swam off and was presumed drowned, and you nearly drowned. After awaking from a coma, you suffer from amnesia, not just of the accident but anything before the accident. That sums it up, right?"

I nod.

"I am telling you that is not the actual story. Your mother killed Dahmon. She shot and killed our father."

It takes a few minutes to recover as the bomb detonates in

199

my head. "That's absurd," I yell out before standing and squaring off against her. "How would you know that or think to presume that?" I turn and escape into the bedroom.

Olivia follows me into the room carrying a paper tablet and a pen and hands them to me. "I know how much you like to write. Think about it and take notes. I won't discuss anything else until tomorrow or until you accept that I am the only one telling you the truth. My name is Kimberly. Let's begin with that truth."

Stunned, sitting cross-legged on the bed, I write "Kimberly" and as many memories as I can recall. Other than the wood cracking and popping, there is no other noise besides the sound of the pen scratching across the paper. I have no memories of my first six years, so I try to recall any words misspoken or whispers I overheard throughout the years.

Several hours later, Kimberly returns to the room and hands me a cell phone. I notice the time, 1400 hours. "Call your bank and have one million dollars transferred to this account number." She hands me a piece of paper.

"I'll transfer it all if you take me back to Roland right now."

"Do what I ask, Dahlia." Kimberly's face is stoic. I call my bank and speak to Jim, the bank president. I ask him to transfer the funds. He asks several safety protocol questions, and I assure him it is me wanting the money moved. It occurs to me someone should've already contacted the bank in case of ransom. Later, Kimberly again feels like talking. From my calculations, I have been gone fifty-one hours.

"Let's say I believe you. What proof do you have? I know Sylvia has secrets. If you know what those secrets are, then I am all ears, but please tell me you didn't go through all this trouble and not have any proof."

"Your mum doesn't have the secrets she thinks she has, and neither do you. Your stepfather, Bob, found me." My mouth drops, and so does my heart. I know he hates me, but why would he seek out any information about Dahmon, let alone find and seek out Kimberly? She continues, "He is the one who told me you received an undisclosed amount in an inheritance. He was curious, so he started visiting courthouses and digging until he found Dahmon's death certificate. Mum knew about you, so I did too, but not about the Halsey's. When I came to America and researched my father's death for myself, I also got a copy of the death certificate." Kimberly digs around in the bag sitting by her feet. "It states that he died of homicide. Under the block, HOW INJURY OCCURRED, it reads: Gun held and fired by Sylvia Halsey. Is that proof enough for you?" Kimberly pulls out a copy of Dahmon's death certificate. I don't want to touch it. I don't want to read it, but she forces me to take it, grabbing and opening my hand and placing the life-altering flat piece of white paper against it.

"Yes." I can't show emotion, and there are no words to explain what I'm feeling anyway. The fact Bob got off his lazy ass and traveled to courthouses researching Mom shocks me more than what he supposedly discovered. How did he find out Dahmon had another child? The man can't use a computer. "Bob must've learned of my inheritance when the attorney contacted Mom to find me. I see why money would make him dig for information, but how would he ever have found out about you if no one else knew you were Dahmon's daughter? Why did he wait so long, and why didn't he ever let Mom know he knew? None of this makes sense."

"I'm unable to answer those questions for you. My mum met Dahmon when she was in Kansas City visiting family. Their affair was brief, but Mum swears she didn't know he was married. But they fought after she found out, and he knocked her around when she threatened to tell your mum. She said she returned to Scotland and didn't know she was pregnant until after getting back. I am the result of their relationship. Dahmon was my father, too. Of course, his rich parents knew nothing about me, but you were not the only heir."

"If you knew this, all you had to do was provide DNA, and they'd have matched it to mine, and you could've contested the will. It's not like there wasn't wide publicity over the Halsey heiress. Why didn't you contact an attorney and contest the will?" I cock my head and ask the question looking at her suspiciously.

"When Bob contacted me—I still don't know how he found out everything—but when he told me this outrageous story, I was as stunned as you are now. Believe me; I am no fan of his. He gave me the creeps just speaking to him on the phone. After his call, I flew to California, researched, and found the death certificate. You could have just as easily. I waited to tell Mum until I verified it for myself. Mum wanted no part of it and didn't want me to have any part. I contacted an American attorney but was told the statute of limitations had passed to contest the will."

"You don't agree, obviously."

"Look, you already had received the funds. The attorney told me there was nothing I could do."

"Okay. So why am I here then? You want me to give you money, which I just did."

"I am entitled to some of it, yes, and that is what you just transferred. That's all I need. I'm not greedy like you. There is more to the story. Tell me, Dahlia; you're a fiction writer. Have you heard that truth is stranger than fiction?"

"Yes, of course."

"Keep that in mind." She remained quiet for a minute, appearing to drift off in memory before continuing, "As I've told you before, I went to university in London, and I met a young barman, jobbing actor." I instantly knew this was about Roland.

I always knew the threats had to do with Roland. She is the woman in the photo. How did I not recognize her? I stand and pace back and forth while listening. She continues. "I fell in love with Roland instantly. I knew he was heartbroken over some American, so I tried to be a friend and provide an ear for him. Months after I met him, we ended up at the same party. Roland was pished, and I listened to him cry into his whiskey while he spoke of his girlfriend, how he couldn't get over her, and he didn't want anyone but her, but somehow the more he drank, the less he cried and the more he wanted me."

She continues, "Then we ran into each other and hooked up again. He didn't let me stay over at his flat the first time we were together, so I expected to get dressed and leave that night. Instead, I thought maybe he also had similar feelings after holding and talking to me for hours before drifting off to sleep. When I woke and opened my eyes, he opened his seconds after, and I whispered, 'I love you.' That was a huge mistake." She slams her hand on her leg. "Take my advice, and don't tell him you love him."

There is so much I want to say, but I don't dare. Kimberly begins again with a sorrowful expression, "I watched as his face tightened. It was like he was suffocating and couldn't speak. Then, Roland swung his long legs over the bed and slid on his trousers. He politely told me he was sorry to let me think he returned any feelings for me. His heart belonged to someone else and always would. He went to the loo, and I quickly dressed and left before he came back out. I knew his heart belonged elsewhere, but I thought maybe he'd forget her." She stops talking for an extended time as though remembering before she continues, "I sometimes wonder if he remembered me until I attended his going-away party. He was leaving for Los Angeles to audition for a big acting role. We left the party together. I took him to my flat, we spent the night together, and we made love. I asked about his lost love, but he only responded, 'I don't want to discuss it,' so we didn't. I never saw or heard from him again."

Kimberly's eyes try to penetrate mine. I've never wanted to hurt a person so bad as her right now. No, that's not true. Bob, always Bob. I stare back at her, looking for anything resembling a conscience or hesitation but see nothing. I search her features for any resemblance or commonality; I see nothing other than a love for Roland. "I'm curious. Is that when you took intimate photos of you two?"

Kimberly laughs. "Yes. That was nearly ten years ago now. I'm not sure why I did it. I don't know whether it was to remember him or have proof. But they did come in handy, didn't they? Several years later, I found out about you and the inheritance."

I feel sorry for Kimberly. I see her pain, and I remember talking about Roland when I returned to New York. That had to be painful for her. "You can wipe that pitiful look off your face. I don't want your pity. He was a complete gentleman, and he was always straightforward. I just wanted more and kept finding little breadcrumbs I could hang on to until he forgot you and loved me. I'm sure you can understand."

"How did you get a camera into my hotel room? I understand you're the one who reserved my hotel rooms, which explains a lot, but how did you get the photo?"

"Dahlia, a person can buy a camera that looks like an alarm clock or a smoke alarm. There are tons of cameras."

"Really?"

"Yes, I've reserved all your hotel rooms since Charlotte hired me. I went there to place the smoke alarm camera the day you were supposed to check in, but instead, you ventured off to Malibu to stay with Roland, I learned from social media posts. So, after you and Roland did show up in Santa Monica, I waited and watched until you checked out to fly back home. Then I printed the photos, took them to the office, and put them in the mailbag before flying here to see my mum."

"How could you have known Roland would stay with me in Santa Monica?"

"You can't be that naïve or stupid, can you?"

She didn't want me to miss any details, and just to make sure I understood what she and Roland had, she repeated some of their nights together twice. "Roland said he liked me as a person, he enjoyed the time we shared, but his heart still belonged to another woman, Dahlia. I hated this woman named Dahlia, and I didn't even know her. I just knew she had Roland's heart, and I wanted him to have it back. So, I googled, white page, and searched Facebook. Do you know there are only ninety-nine results for Dahlia on Facebook? I searched everyone and anything named Dahlia and always came up empty-handed. Then, as fate would have it, I was contacted by a man named Bob. When he said his stepdaughter, Dahlia, I thought I would die. What were the chances that his stepdaughter Dahlia and Roland's Dahlia were the same? I had information about my father, a sister, and Roland's lost love. It was all just handed to me, so I knew I had to act on it. What were the chances the same Dahlia could have ruined two aspects of my life? I wanted to know what you had that I didn't. Anyway, I moved to New York and watched and waited."

I'm unsure if she wanted me to answer that question, and I thought better of even trying, so I shut my mouth. The idea a person could place a camera in a room, and I wouldn't even know, was absurd; the fact Bob knew about my inheritance from the time the attorney found Mom to get my location, Bob had been planning something. "Was it Bob's plan for you to kidnap me?"

"It was discussed. He was supposed to do it in the States. I was supposed to get close to you and schedule a book signing in Santa Monica where he planned to abduct you, but then he found out about the book, kicked your mum out of the house, and all hell broke loose. When Roland showed up at your signing, I knew it was a means to end my long struggle, and I had to do something. Bob wants you to suffer, and he wants a share of whatever I get."

"So, you plan to take the money and not give him any. And you've told me he was in on it, and you said you don't plan to kill me, so I assume you want him to take the fall for all of it. How did you connect Dahlia Frost to Frances Slater? You obviously discovered that before Bob, yet you didn't tell him about the book. What would make you kidnap me and demand the money instead of contacting me? You knew who I was and a lot about me at the time. Couldn't you have just come to me and told me the truth?" I say all this out loud, but I'm unsure if I am talking to her or talking it all out in my head. I have kept my mouth shut until now. I'm physically hurt, shaken to my core, and exhausted from lies. I pace back and forth before saying, "Of course not. How stupid of me to think anyone can speak the truth."

"I just so happened to read *Daddy Issues* by Frances Slater. I am a publicist in the publishing business. The story was familiar, and I couldn't believe my luck again. When the publicist position opened, it was an omen that I was indeed supposed to meet you. When you returned from London, I knew I had to do something. You couldn't take everything that I love. If neither of us ended up with him, that was bearable, but for him to seek you out and make such a grand entrance was all I could stand."

"That doesn't answer the question. Why didn't you just come to me after discovering who I was? If I had known this entire story before leaving for London, I guarantee his grand entrance wouldn't have gone the way it did. Well, it isn't his fault. How could he have known you and I were related? This is so messed up."

She continues as if I didn't speak, "I was told we are sisters after you received the inheritance, and I was envious, but my mum was adamant I not say anything or do anything to upset you. She's gone now, so her wishes don't count where you are concerned. Why couldn't I just come to you? Tell me something, why is it always about you? It's as if we are twins in the same womb, but you suck up all the nutrients and grow while I wither away and die. I deserve at least some of the inheritance from our father. Wouldn't you agree?" Kimberly is crying, and I want to comfort her, so I reach for her hand, but she pulls away. "I want to hate you, Dahlia, but I don't because you didn't know any of this, and none of it is your fault. I don't want to live in your shadow anymore."

I see the lights and hear the car pull up but don't give it much thought since Kimberly doesn't—at least not until Kimberly's huge friend, whose name is never mentioned, comes back into the cabin. His arms are holding a small bag of supplies. I watch him scan the room for Kimberly. His smile turns to a look of rage as he sees her tears. I see the hatred for me cross his face. When he grabs my arms, pulls me from the chair, and then pushes me into the bedroom, I am terrified of what he might do to me. I yell to Kimberly through the door, "I'm sorry, Kimberly. I don't know what else to say."

I lay on the bed, listening to her cry, and hear the huge man tell her, "Take the money and leave her 'ere. We need to go. Her face is being flashed all over the telly. I did what ye said. I left the second ransom note telling him where to drop money."

While lying here, I remove my Garmin from its hiding spot. I press the button and am shocked it comes on as I cover it to hide any noise or light. I press the walk button to start the GPS. Hopefully, it'll provide my location before the battery dies.

Praying someone knows my location by now, I listen to their conversation.

Kimberly tells him, "I made her transfer a million too. Did anyone see you?"

"Nay, I pinned it on the gates at his farmhouse. He'll find it as soon as he enters the gates again. Ye told her your story. Ye have her sympathy. Ye have a million and maybe two if ye lucky. What else do ye want? We need to go, Kimberly. They're looking for her, and ye ken it."

"I want them both to suffer. You know that. I want his heart to be broken a thousand times each time he broke mine, but I can't hurt her."

"I can. She may be bonnie, but I think she's a snooty bitch."

"No, since Mum passed, she truly is the only family I have left, not that she and I will ever be family, but I can't hurt her, and you won't. Understand me? You're right; we will leave her here, and they'll find her, or she'll find her way back or not. They'll soon question why his maintenance man is nowhere to be found and start looking for you. She doesn't have a phone; they can't track her. We'll leave in the morning. I still want to talk to her a little more."

The huge man says, "We should go tonight, while it's dark and no one sees us."

It takes a long time before drifting off to sleep. Mr. huge man startles me when he unlocks the door. When I step into the living area, Kimberly has food for me. I don't realize how hungry I am until I smell the food. "Are you hungry? You need to eat?"

"Yes. Kimberly, did you send me all the threats to scare or warn me?" Kimberly glares at me. "Yes, more like to give you hints. I put the invitation and the photos in with your mail. I took the package of baby items to Roland's house."

"How did you get through the gates? Did you break into his house and break the mirror? What about the Dear Jane letter?"

"No, I didn't break into his house; I made friends with his maintenance man, whom you've now met, and I entered through the side door one afternoon with him. I left the package."

"And broke the mirror?"

"Yes, I remember reading that mirror in his flat one of the nights I was with him. I hated it then. I know how creepy it sounds, but I found his bedroom and opened his closet. I took a shirt and sprayed it with his cologne. When I was leaving the room, I saw the mirror right before I opened the door, so I took a small screwdriver out of my bag and stabbed it right in the center, imagining your face. It shattered. I thought it was fitting. I didn't write you a Dear Jane letter, though. Roland wrote you the Dear Jane letter and then regretted it. I remember his buddies mentioning it when he was whining about you not answering your phone."

I don't want to give her the satisfaction of seeing my reaction to this unknown information. She knows how much those letters hurt me. "I'm assuming Charlotte mentioned I was pregnant. Is that how you found out? What about the flowers?"

"Yes, she slipped, and I swore I'd not say anything. What flowers?"

"The black dahlias."

"I didn't send you black dahlias. How did I not know about them?"

"Are you forevermrshughes?"

"No, but I've read her comments. Roland must truly have a stalker, or you do."

I sit quietly and absorb all she has said. I believe everything she has told me. I eat in silence and I am proud I show no emotion about Roland's betrayal and my brokenness. If she is right, he lied to me about receiving a Dear John letter and writing me the Dear Jane letter. He must've recognized

Kimberly in the photo as well. Oh my God, Maggie's words rico-
chet in my head. She said he had mentioned a Dear Jane letter
at the cast party. She didn't say Dear John letter. How would
she know if he didn't know about a Dear Jane letter? He must
think I am stupid. I hate him. He looked into my eyes and lied
when I begged for the truth. How could he sleep in my bed, pull
me close, and live with himself knowing our life is based on a
lie? I hate them all. Mom shot and killed Dahmon and left that
out. At least Mom didn't try to lie; she just omitted every important detail of my life. I have no more tears to cry because all I
feel for these liars is resentment and disgust. Maybe I will just
stay here in this cabin.

It is morning; I wrap a blanket around me and tippy-toe out
of the cabin. It is chilly and windy, and I want to clear my head.
Walking to the rear of the cabin, avoiding the mud and standing
water from all the rain, I look out over the valley and mountains.
I am stunned by its beauty. I already discovered we're sitting
high on a cliff and understand why Kimberly warned me not to
try to escape. I remind myself of all that is right in the world. I
worked too hard to pull myself out of a darkness I didn't create.
No one who created that abyss was there to lend a hand or even
an ear to my healing; I won't let the sins of my mother or my
fiancé send me into a spiral. I hug my trembling body tighter as
the similarities of the hole I was placed in two nights ago and the
bottomless pit from the hypnosis swirl in my memory, but I am
older, stronger, and wiser and won't fall apart this time. I love
Sylvia and can live without her, but I don't want to. I love
Roland with every beat of my heart, but I can live without him. I
just don't want to. Why have they left me no choice? I've done it
before for over half my life. My child will never have to live with
secrets or lies.

Kimberly's voice invades my thoughts. I call her, letting her
know I've not disappeared, but she is either frantic or angry

when she comes around the back of the cabin and sees me. I can't distinguish the panic in her volume. "What are you doing out here? I told you not to come out here."

"No, you told me not to try to escape, and I am not trying. I needed to clear my head, so I came outside. What now, Kimberly?"

"I am leaving, and you'll never see me again. That's why I need the money. I'm sure the police and Roland have figured out who I am and know I have you. Your wedding is in two days and Charlotte must've arrived for your wedding."

"Wedding? Oh, yeah, I forgot about that. Kimberly, we can go to the police together. I don't have to press charges. We can work this out." She looks at me, and I wonder why I want to help her. I understand her pain but not her method. She should've just told me.

"You need to come back into the cabin. We're going."

We both turn toward the cabin as we hear things breaking and smashing. I hear Charlotte's voice, and then a gunshot and a scream. As I turn to run to the front, Kimberly grabs me and pulls me in front of her like a shield. "This isn't necessary, Kimberly. No one will hurt you." I didn't doubt anything she had said until she decided to use me as a shield instead of letting me help her out of this mess. Maybe her mother told her Dahmon wasn't her father before she died, but the "almighty dollar" wheels had already begun to turn. Maybe Bob had it wrong. I am shocked to see Charlotte run around the side of the cabin. She has her hands up and palms out.

"Olivia, I mean Kimberly, let Dahlia go. We know this is about you and Roland. He told the police everything." Charlotte turns and looks behind her. I see Roland as he rounds the side of the cabin, holding his arm and bleeding. The huge man isn't there, and I assume he and Roland scuffled. I saw the gun tucked in the belt of the huge man's pants. I want to run to him and make sure he is all right, but I remember he is part of the problem. He's alive, and that's all I can concern myself with now. The wind picks up, and I can't hear what Charlotte is saying, which means Kimberly can't either.

Kimberly tightens her grip on me. She screams, "Stay back and keep the police back. You don't know the entire story the way you think you do. Do they, Dahlia?"

I shake my head and tell Kimberly, "Please let me go. I will talk to them for you. I will do what I can to see you aren't charged with kidnapping. Let me help you."

Two police officers are now at the rear of the cabin with tasers drawn. "Let go and step away from her." To my surprise, she does. She lets go, shoves me forward, and steps back as far as she can without falling.

"Please, Kimberly, I will help. We will take care of the liars together, I promise." I turn and face Roland, pointing at him. "Please, I promise I will help you." I look at the police. "Please don't hurt her; she's my sister." I glance back at Roland and Charlotte to see the shock on their faces.

The wind picks up, blowing increasingly harder. Her dark hair whips around her face blocking her expression. "Too late, you take care of yourself and the wee bairn," she yells as the wind slows and her voice carries. Her hair quits blowing, and I can see her eyes as she weeps. Charlotte and I motion for her to come to us, but she looks at Roland. He takes steps toward her, and with his uninjured arm, he motions for her to come to him. He extends his uninjured arm toward her. "I have only loved one man, and I couldn't make you love me, Roland. I had no idea the woman you longed for all those years was, in fact, my sister. I guess it is sweet justice that both of you live with the memory of all this truth," she says to Roland.

"Dahlia, I'm forgettable. Just ask Roland." She searches

Roland's face and settles on his eyes as she steps backward off the side of the cliff.

"No!" we all scream at the same time. I crawl over to the edge and brace myself on my arms, looking down into a familiar abyss.

Chapter 17

Sorry

May 14th

I jolt up, gasping for breath, afraid to open my eyes and be in the dark. At least with my eyes open, I know I can see. I rock my body back and forth for comfort to fall back to sleep, only to be awakened what feels like minutes later when the light shines through the open curtains. Unless someone is robbed of the light, you can't appreciate the burst of energy and power the sunshine provides to our soul. Roland is lying beside me, wide awake and staring at me. Today is supposed to be our wedding day, but the only thing I am grateful for is that it is daylight. The day I was rescued, we both lay in the same hospital room as I withdrew further from him; I was hooked to IVs and his arm was treated for the gunshot wound. A nurse turned off the light and closed the door behind her to our room, and I was in the closet again, screaming for someone to let me out. Roland tried to soothe me but couldn't. After being sedated, I knew I could no longer be blinded to the dark or lies. I watched the vision in my hypnosis come to fruition, and I'm fighting those same monsters in my head again. I want to forgive

214

Roland and move forward, but I can't. Fool me once; shame on you. Fool me twice; shame on me. And I am no one's fool.

I need to talk to him. I've not spoken but a few words since he rescued me. I reach out and place my hand near the wound on his right shoulder. It breaks my heart that he was wounded saving me, but I need to be in control and touch him on my terms. My glassy eyes search his deep-blue sorrowful eyes for answers and reassurance. He can't give me what's been taken from me, but I know he would if he could. He fights to keep his distance when I know all he wants is to fix what has been broken inside me. I try to tell him what Kimberly said to me with a voice barely above a whisper, attempting to express her brokenness adequately. It is hard to feel sympathy for Kimberly and her actions, but I feel horrible for her death.

"I'm so sorry," Roland whispers.

"It's not your fault. This could've happened in Santa Monica and supposedly was initially planned. Maybe if I had known all the secrets, I'd have made different decisions, and Kimberly would still be alive. You told me to be strong. I am strong, but I let my guard down, believing you could protect me. I trusted those who love me would finally be honest with me."

Roland reaches for me with his hurt arm and cringes. "I know your arm hurts, Roland." He adjusts and reaches for me with his uninjured arm, but I pull away.

"Not compared to my heart. Let me hold you," he pleads.

"You're injured," I tell him as I roll away from him. I hope the excuse will be enough to make him understand that I don't want to be held. My heart hurts, too. His arms can't protect me, just like Mom failed to protect me.

"I can manage with one arm. I might as well get up." His voice is tense and injured. The room is quiet other than the sounds of my sniffing. Roland throws back the covers and gets out of bed. I watch him go, but I can't go after him. Instead, I get out of bed and pace around the bedroom. Only as far as the other side of the room before I end up back in the bed, crying. Sometime during the night, I decided to return to New York. I have to try to erase the images in my head. I kept seeing Kimberly's face staring into Roland's eyes as I stared into hers before she stepped off that cliff. I don't forgive how she handled her hurt or frustration, and it's obvious she had come completely unglued after her mother's death, but I can't blame her. I blame Bob.

I only force myself out of the bedroom because I want coffee more than anything else. While standing in the kitchen, I notice Roland lying on the duvet. I'm unsure if he is asleep; I want to kiss him awake, but I don't. I can't be near him, or I won't leave. I need time away from him to think. Instead, I tippy-toe back into the bedroom, drink my coffee, and make phone calls. Pulling out paper, I write a list:

1) Call the coroner, offer to pay Kimberly's burial expenses if her body is recovered, and ask for a DNA test before she is buried.

2) Book a flight home for today.

3) Call Charlotte.

I dial her number.

"Hello," she answers.

"Charlotte, where are you?"

"I'm in a hotel here in Glasgow. I was there to see you yesterday, but Roland said you weren't doing well. I didn't want to disturb you and came back to the hotel. How are you?"

"Change your flight home, please; I need you. Roland said Jane made all the necessary calls to postpone the wedding, and I'm going home today. I'll screenshot the flight info as soon as I get my ticket and see you on board."

"Okay, Dahlia, if you are sure about this, I'll see you there."

Ticket purchased, I lay the open suitcase on the bed and

begin packing the folded clothes I have already sorted. I try to think of a solution, anything where this whole situation is forgiven, where I can look at Mom or Roland's faces again without feeling betrayed. I can't. Roland's face shows signs of exhaustion to match my own as he enters the bedroom. His hair is disheveled, and his face unshaven.

"You're fucking leaving? You've got to be kidding me. I stare at him dressed in sleep shorts and no shirt on. I am torn. I want to run into his arms, and I want to run away. I can tell he didn't mean to speak to me so loudly by the shock of his expression and quick steps toward me, reaching out for me. "Please stay," he whispers, kneels in front of me, wrapping his arms around our baby and me, and lays his head in my lap. "Please don't leave me, not again."

I run my fingers through his hair and bend my body over his. "I don't know how to stay; I need some time," I assure him or try to ensure us both. He rocks back on his knees before standing to leave the room. I stay in the bedroom, trying to avoid his eyes, arms, and that look I can't place—anger mixed with sadness, maybe. I don't want to discuss this. I pace back and forth, and all I can think about is getting out. I want to go. I hear him moving around the otherwise silent house where even the air is fragile. I don't want to breathe too heavily and cause a ripple in the silence.

Picking up the wad of snotty wet Kleenex beside me on the made bed, I carry it to the bathroom tin. When I come back into the bedroom, Roland appears in the doorway, leaning against the doorframe with one foot in and one foot out. It is symbolic of how I feel about our relationship right now. I want him to understand that I need time, but the more he speaks, the more I hear his lies echo in my ears and the angrier I become. Doesn't he understand how much truth has been dumped on me the last few days? And he dares stand here looking angry and wanting my justification for leaving? I don't want to say anything to hurt him further. "I want to go to my home. I'm angry with you for knowingly hiding secrets from me. You know how important the truth is to me. Most of all, I'm angry at myself because I know how dangerous it is to be the one who loves the most. Shame on me." I turn from him, zip up my suitcase, and pull it off the bed purposely to avoid his eyes.

He makes a sound I don't recognize, so I turn to face him. Roland's face is tight, and I know he is fighting back as many emotions as I am, both of us trying not to spew things that can never be taken back. "I thought this was your home too. I thought we agreed to raise our child here and together. Can't you make peace because I believed I was doing the right thing and protecting you?"

"Well, then you failed because something did happen to me, and that's because of Bob and his hatred of me. But the lies and omissions you and Mom made and kept from me made it possible. Kimberly couldn't have gotten near me if I'd been armed with the truth. You recognized her and hid that from me. You told me it took Charlotte recognizing Olivia in the photos at the police station and speaking up for you to tell the police her name was Kimberly. Do you not see how the lies cost her life? That inheritance was hers too. What is wrong with all of you? No one who said they were protecting me protected me."

"No one protected you? You love the most?" He points his finger at me and steps toward me as he shakes his head. "You are so full of shit. You didn't search for me. I searched for you. You got rid of every physical memory of us. What did you hold on to? Nothing, you trashed every picture, letter, card, and theatre ticket. You told me that yourself. For God's sake, I carried around a mirror for nineteen years and have every photo we've had taken. You don't love the most or unconditionally; that's me." He blows the air out of his lungs forcefully. "What about

218

the baby? Are you going to prevent me from being in my child's life? I don't deserve this, and our child doesn't. I won't allow my child not to know me or be in my life like your father wasn't in yours."

"Since he was dead, there wasn't much choice, was there? I don't know what I want, but I would never keep our child away from you. You can be the baby's father and not my husband. They aren't synonymous. I can't marry you right now; I know that." I remove my engagement ring and lay it on the dresser.

"This isn't you. The Dahlia I love...." Roland utters as he follows me out of his bedroom and into the guest bedroom to hang my wedding gown out of his sight, preventing a constant reminder. I freeze mid-step, slowly put my foot down and turn to him.

"The Dahlia you love? This is me, and you helped create this version of me." My words are loud and angry.

He finishes his sentence softly, "...forgives." I watch the tears stream down his face, but I can't let that phase me. He removes his ring, lays it on top of mine, then leaves the room. Why couldn't he give me some time? Now he wants to tell his truths.

Half an hour later, pulling my suitcase behind me, I step into the same room as Roland. He steps in front of me, one of his hands grabs the handle of my suitcase, and the other grabs my wrist. When he looks into my eyes, it is all I can do not to cry. I need time. We might survive if he would allow me some time to cope and heal from all this. "I've spent days figuring out how to help you and what to say, but I finally figured out there are no words that can give you back what was lost. Instead, I figured out why you have to run. You're leaving because you were reminded of what it feels like not to have control over something that happened to you. And God forbid you don't have control in or out of the bedroom or have to "depend" on someone else, let alone trust them. I am sorry that you went through something

terrible and had to face that darkness again. I truly feel responsible and would do anything to fix this, but no, you will run back
to your tower high above Manhattan, where you can live vicari-
ously through the people below." He stops, and I believe he is
finished, so I try to pull loose from his grip, but he holds on to
my wrist while tilting my head toward him.

Then he continues, "I have news for you; those people are
willing to take chances every day, even if they fail, even if something knocks them on their arse. You're retreating; you've given
up and lost your fight—shame on you. You're leaving me and
taking our future and baby with you because you're mad, and
running is all you know. The military, your divorce, moving to
New York to get away from Sylvia, and now running from me.
There is nothing admirable about falling on your sword, and
guess what, you take you with you wherever you run." He lets
go of me and steps out of my way.

What can I say to his perceptive observation? It takes me a
second to come back with my response to my worthy opponent.
"There is nothing admirable about lying, either. You pretend to
know me. If you do, then you know I am never stuck. God gave
me knees that bend, hands that pray, and feet to move. No one
will ever tell me when to bend, how to pray, or how far and fast I
can move. As I said, I am never stuck." I let go of the suitcase,
step in front of him, stretch on my tippy-toes, wrap my arms
around him, and bend his cheek to meet my lips, but he turns
his face away.

"Goodbye, Dahlia." I grab the handle of my suitcase as
forcefully as possible, stomp to the front door as fast as possible,
sling the front door open as powerfully as possible, and take one
step out of the house before he adds, "I dare ya to stay."

"That won't work this time. Goodbye, Roland." I don't look
back when I say it. I refuse to let him drive me to the airport or

220

ride with the driver. How do I make peace with all this information? Kimberly was right; I should've done my research.

The paparazzi surround Charlotte and me at the airport, snapping photos and screaming out questions they want me to answer about the kidnapping. I keep my head down as the bodyguard escorts us to our flight. Charlotte holds my hand as the airplane lifts off the runway. "So much for the media forgetting about Roland and me," I tell Charlotte.

"Roger will meet us at our gate when we arrive. You might want to think about making a major purchase."

I glance at Charlotte and shrug, "You mean an airplane?" She nods, and it occurs to me that soon the news will be out about the cancelation of our wedding, and the baby will be here. She may be right. At this point, there is not enough security that could make me feel safe.

I am instantly terrified I may never see Roland again. I close my eyes, and all I see is his face. I lay my head on the pillow against the window and hear his words: "I've loved your memory for so long that nothing else mattered when I found you. If I could, I'd do anything, give anything, to make your pain disappear. I wish I could take back writing that letter, lying about it, but I can't. If you leave Whisky Girl, you can't take it back, and we can't fix this apart. We don't want this to be a part of our story. You left with my heart one other time; I guess I can survive it again, but don't lie to yourself about why you're leaving, and don't lie to me."

I try not to think about the argument. I want to escape Roland and his words, but I can't. I sit up and readjust my pillow, knowing I won't rest anytime soon.

Chapter 18

Skyscraper

June 16th

My apartment high above Manhattan lights up the sky as all the lights shine through the glass walls. I keep tucked away where I know the baby and I will be safe, in my tower, as Roland calls it. No one but Charlotte in or out. Roger and a second security guard will see to that. Still afraid of my shadow and leaving the apartment, I am forced to attend my monthly prenatal visit. The obstetrician can't be bribed to do a home visit. "Hey, Dahlia, you better not be in pajamas," Charlotte chirps.

"Hey, Charlotte, I am in my pajamas because they fit, and I still haven't shopped for maternity clothes." I remain seated on the sectional and flash my best fake smile as she enters the apartment. "Tomorrow, I am leaving, and after my obstetrician appointment, I will go and buy maternity clothes that fit. But they will be just as loose and baggie as my pajamas. Does that make you feel better?"

"It does. That doesn't explain why you've not run a brush through that nest on top of your head." She shakes her head as if shaking my image from her head before she changes the subject. "How are your security guys working out? I noticed the one outside the elevator is hot." Charlotte fans her face and nudges my elbow.

"Go for it."

"I'm kidding. I'm going on vacation soon and thought maybe you and I could take a trip together. Maybe back to Scotland so you and Roland can talk."

"I am happy you are going. Tell him I said hi. I want to see the doctor and ensure the baby's growing the way he or she should. I won't be returning to Scotland for a while."

"Do you know what the wee bairn's sex is?" Charlotte lays her hand on my belly. I don't miss her attempt at a Scottish accent either.

"No, not yet; an ultrasound is scheduled for tomorrow, but I don't want to have it done without Roland, and since I don't know what I'm going to do with that entire situation, I'll wait." I'm not stupid; I know she wants to know, without asking, my frame of mind after a month of being home.

She sits on the new white sectional, and if she notices, she doesn't say anything. If she plans on staying, I guess I ought to be nice. I pour us both a glass of tea. "Follow me; I want to show you something." We go upstairs to the bedroom that I made into the new nursery. She takes steps directly to the crib and follows the curvature of the white wood frame up into the Whisky Girl tartan canopy with her hand. The white crib stands out against the accent charcoal gray wall—the room's decorated in highland cows and tartan colors. I made a sign, "Welcome to my crib," and framed it in white. All I need to finish is a wooden name to place on the wall above the crib. We turn to leave the room, and she notices the photo I taped to the lower portion of the inside of the door.

"What is that for?"

"The baby will know Roland's face. Eventually, he or she will be crawling, right?"

"So, the baby won't see its father's face until after he or she is crawling?" She makes a grimacing frown. "The room is beautiful, Dahlia."

I close the door behind us. Charlotte moves about the apartment, entering the master bedroom. She notes, "You have all new furniture. When did you have time to get all this done?" She picks up the framed photo of Roland and me that I have sitting by my bed. She looks either amazed or shocked, and I can't figure out which. "Seems you'll remember his face as well."

"I planned and paid for all the nursery items here and at Roland's simultaneously. I contacted the store and told them I needed the nursery done here immediately, and if they expedited, I would buy an entire household of furniture. I can't believe how fast they scheduled the delivery." The real reason for the new furniture is my own business. I couldn't lay in the bed where Roland and I had made love. I couldn't sit on the sectional where we made love. The dining room table had to go. I should have the kitchen island and shower ripped out, but on second thought, I should move.

"You're not going back to him, are you, Dahlia?" Charlotte hangs her head in disappointment. I wonder if she is disappointed in him or me. "I understand why he lied to you. It will help if you put yourself in his shoes." I get my answer. Charlotte is disappointed in me and my decision to leave Scotland and Roland.

Turning my back to her and descending the stairs, I reply, "He lied to me, Charlotte, about writing the Dear Jane and receiving a Dear John without explaining why he wrote it or lied." Standing in the kitchen, I sit down at the island before continuing, "I could maybe forgive that, but when he recognized Kimberly's face in the photo, why did he choose to hide that from me? Roland said he wanted to protect me. I wonder if that is the excuse Sylvia will use. She knew the monster I was living with growing up, and no one did anything about that. Who does that? I can't deal with Sylvia yet. She is ill, and I need to be in a better, kinder mind before looking into her face. Roland is a grown-ass man and can deal with the consequences until I'm ready to forgive him." I've survived the chaos brought on by others and became responsible for their irresponsible behaviors. I'm over being the one to forgive.

Charlotte shakes her head. "He may not be around by the time that happens; how sad for your child. Why should he or she pay the price of your unforgiveness?"

I try to end the conversation. "I will call Roland after my doctor's appointment. That is all I can give him. Please, Charlotte. He has finally quit calling and texting." I beg her to leave it alone, but she doesn't.

"Have you ever lied, Dahlia? Or better yet, have you ever told a half-truth or white lie? No one is perfect. I hate to be the one to burst your bubble, but not even you. No matter how far you run, how much you spend, or put your spin on a story, we all make mistakes, and you need to learn to forgive others and yourself. You are the most conflicted person I have ever known. You are strong yet frail. You forgive but never forget. You love with your whole heart until you don't. I'm going to tell you something you won't want to hear."

"You've already said several somethings I don't want to hear." I change positions and rooms as if doing so will change the topic. It doesn't. I await her wisdom.

"You're so fucked up that you make fifty shades look like a children's book."

"What?" Looking at my best friend, who can and usually does say anything she wants to me—things I'd never allow anyone else to say, I'm aghast and reply, "Don't beat around the bush, Charlotte. So, I'm more fucked up than a dominant because I'm sick of being lied to? I don't see you dating and putting your heart on the line." I run my hands through my tangled hair before putting my hand in the air to stop her from talking. "You know what? You're right; I am. It's about fucking time society has to deal with the women it created. We can be sexy, but god forbid we have too much sex, we can be loving, but oh my god, don't be obsessive or smothering, we can be rich, but we can't have too much power, we can be angry and hurt but crazy isn't allowed. I think it's about damn time I speak up for what I want and put some boundaries in place for the people who want to be in my life. I'm done listening to opinions like they're gospel. I may be conflicted, but at least I put my heart out there again to get broken."

Charlotte shakes her head and then reaches out to hug me. "We're not talking about me right now."

I step back, "No, we're not. You want to talk about me."

She continues, "I'm on your side, and I'm on this baby's side. But you will never be happy if you constantly expect more from people than they can give. Love and happiness can be messy but worth it. Please, pull your big girl panties up, put on one of your power suits, a pair of Louies, and dig deep to bring back the powerhouse I knew before all this began," she said before she left.

I want a whiskey. At least I learned one thing while pregnant; I don't have an alcohol problem. I have a "need to be in control" problem, so I've heard twice now, as Charlotte just pointed out and Roland pointed out a month ago. I was happy she went home.

The following morning, when Roger opens the door to the SUV, I am happy to see that Charlotte is sitting in the vehicle and is accompanying me to my doctor's appointment. I want someone with me, so she'll have to do. She needs to be on my side.

We listen to the baby's heartbeat, and I measure twenty weeks. The doctor seems concerned until I tell him, "The baby's daddy is a big guy, and there is no way I can be any farther along than nineteen weeks."

"I want to do an ultrasound," the doctor states. I agree to do it next month on my next visit. "Fine, you will also have your glucose test at that time. It would be a good time for your husband to come if you want to find out the sex of your baby."

I nod. Charlotte smiles a big smile.

Charlotte and I spend the rest of the day shopping. Standing at the checkout, wearing the new designer shorts and jacket, I pay for my purchases and then change my shoes to the new pair of Louboutin sneakers. I look pretty amazing if I say so myself. New clothes and Louboutins can fix even the worst of days. I could get used to this more casual look.

"You look so cute," Charlotte snaps a photo of me, "especially when you don't wear your resting bitch face." She smiles big and holds up two thumbs. "I'm posting this on your new social media page so your fans can see your progress. Pretty soon, we'll have a photo of a new book to keep them busy, but they need to see Dahlia Frost."

"I don't think I will publish any more books, Charlotte." I've been thinking about this and figuring out how to discuss the topic. Now is as good a time as any, I suppose. She looks at me with shock on her face.

"I don't believe that for a minute. Your stories need telling, scars, successes, victories, and messes."

"All of the rules I broke in the name of needing to be loved have cost so many and caught up with me. I've paid a high price. Everyone who knows or loves me pays a high price."

"I'm sorry I hired Kimberly. I had no way of knowing, but I

guarantee I will double and triple-check references. Her death is not your fault. I haven't paid a high price, but even if I do, you're worth it. The truth hurts." Charlotte hugs me, and I feel the ice around my heart crack.

Since we are already in public, I agree to lunch at one of Charlotte's favorite restaurants. When leaving, I am recognized by two very lovely women wanting photos and autographs. I reluctantly agree. Another woman approaches us while signing my autograph, and I wave for Roger to allow it. The third woman's words leave me speechless, "She dumped Roland Hughes; I wouldn't have her autograph if she paid me to take it." Then she walks away. The women waiting for me to finish their autographs assure me I have actual fans and deserve my affirmation. Charlotte laughs loudly, so I laugh, too, instead of crying. I'm stunned because all I've done during this pregnancy is cry.

Since I'm in a surprisingly good mood for a change, Charlotte and I go back to my apartment and scroll through Netflix. Charlotte stops on a new rom-com, "I've wanted to see that. Can we watch it?"

"A rom-com? I guess, but don't get mad when I bawl like a baby. You should've seen me watching the last season of Roland's series. I went through an entire box of tissue. Just wait until you get pregnant, Charlotte. You'll see." Two hours later, bawling like a baby, I have a change of heart and decide to offer forgiveness.

"I'm going to call my mother."

"What? I wanted you to watch this because I wanted you to call Roland. Don't you see the similarities?" Charlotte slaps her hand down on her leg and stands up. "I've already watched this movie three times, Dahlia."

I laugh. "Yes, I realized that as you quoted lines throughout the movie. I spoke with Roland the other day when he called to ask me to accompany him to his premiere. I told him I couldn't go, but we would talk soon. I didn't mention it to you because I don't want you to get your hopes up, Charlotte."

She hugs me goodbye, "It will work out; I know it."

I call my mother. "Hello."

"Hello, Mom. How are you feeling?" I take a sip of my water.

"I'm doing all right. The doctor prescribed a new medicine to control my shaking, but I can still stand with milk in my hands and make a milkshake."

Spitting the water across the kitchen island, I laugh hard. She still has a sense of humor, at least. But I'm still angry at her and change my tone, "Mom, I'm coming to see you in a couple of days, depending on what day I can make it happen. I'm just giving you a heads up that we need to talk."

"I know. I wanted to call you the minute you were found safe, but Roland called me and told me everything that happened and everything you found out. I've been waiting for you to want to talk to me. Come on home, Dahlia, and let's talk. It's time. I love you."

After hanging up the phone, I scroll through my new social media accounts. I forgot that Charlotte posted the photo of me and my belly. The page has thousands of likes, hearts, and comments. Two particular comments jump out at me. One from Daniel stands out. "I would've never imagined you could be more beautiful, but you are...." Then one comment from Roland stands out. "That's my Whisky Girl and wee baby. I am sending all my love from across the ocean." I close the apps and put the phone down. Roland is honoring my wish to give me space even though I know how much that must hurt him and how unfair it has been. He shouldn't learn of our progress over social media.

Chapter 19

Easy On Me

The landing bothered me more than usual. However, exiting the airport was worse than the landing as sweat rolled off me. I attribute it to pregnancy more than the California heat. The air-conditioning blowing directly on me from the vents in the rental car provides instant relief. On the short drive to Mom's house, I thought I'd be frantic over what to say to her, but all I could think about was changing into more comfortable clothing, and I'm happy I packed maternity shorts and tees.

"You look exhausted, Dahlia. But let me see you. Can I touch your belly?" Mom asks.

"Yes, of course. You would be surprised how many people reach over and touch my belly."

"Oh, there is nothing like the draw and glow of a pregnant woman. Wait until Roland can see how much your belly has grown. I'm just so happy I'm going to be a grandma."

"Yeah, anyway, I don't want to discuss Roland. I want to discuss the topics you have avoided discussing with me for years, even though others knew. I came to listen. Today is the day. I'm not staying long." I won't be rude, but I can't be sweet and loving. I pull my suitcase into the guest room and return to the kitchen where Mom is standing. I am angry at this woman, yet seeing her upset upsets me. How could she?

"I understand you are angry, and I don't want to inflict stress on you by being here. So, if you don't have long, we ought to get straight to it then, huh?" She pulls out two envelopes from her desk, puts one back, and lays one in front of me on the kitchen table as I sit and scoot the chair farther away than usual. "I was hoping you wouldn't read this letter until after I died." She pours us both a glass of lemonade. "Let's go out on the veranda instead of sitting here."

"I'm hot. Is it hot out there?"

"No. It's nice. Come on, and let's get comfortable. I have the drinks. You grab the envelope." Making myself comfortable, I am grateful for the pleasant breeze and getting off my feet. I am surprisingly relaxed. Mom doesn't need to see the chaos this situation has stirred up inside me. I guzzle my lemonade as Mom instructs me, "Read the letter first, then I'll answer whatever questions you have, Dahlia. I'm not going to relive this for you or anyone." I need to read a letter. I find that cowardly, but I open it. It is barely legible because of her shaking. Again, I wish she would just talk to me about this.

My Dearest Dahlia,

I enjoyed our visit. I wish it would've been under better circumstances. I appreciate you coming to my rescue and all you have done to help me settle in a new house. While you were here, we were able to talk about so many things that seem to have been deemed taboo between us for years. I know a lot of that had to do with Bob. He was always jealous of my love for you, Dahlia. He had to be first in my heart. He demanded all my time, and unlike you, I need someone. Don't think I don't know that you needed me more than him; you were a teenager, and he was a grown man, but it was a self-centered decision I made when you looked at me and told me, "Don't leave him for me because I'm not staying here for you." I decided to look out for my security. Not unlike a different time, I had to choose to protect myself so that I could save you. I had to look out for both our safety and security.

I can't read this letter with your eyes or your heart, so I have no idea what you will do with the information I am about to provide. I must admit that I fear revealing this to you, but I know it's time. When you told me you were writing your novel, I had no idea that you would get it published. I had no idea how successful the book would be, but I was grateful you'd written it under a pen name. Now that your face and identity are associated with it, I know it is only a matter of time before the world knows who I am and my story is revealed. I'm afraid your reconnection with Roland will only speed up the inevitable. I told you the story about your memory loss. I could do nothing to prevent it other than I should have never told Dahmon I wanted the divorce. I should've just sought the divorce and moved out without Dahmon knowing or being able to find us. But I didn't. That day will forever be engraved in my memory. After he split my head open with the butt of the rifle and left me lying in a pool of my own blood, he put you in his car and drove you across the country to his parent's house. I assume they told him to bring you back to me. He had a car accident and hydroplaned off into the lake. Did he swim off and leave you to drown? That question has always plagued me. You almost died, and he was presumed drowned. But by the Grace of God, you survived and didn't have a brain injury other than amnesia.

What I didn't tell you is what happened to Dahmon. Let me make it clear: I did not lie to you. You ask, and I told you he had an accident. He did. There is more to the story that you need to know.

I pause, reading the letter, "Mom, when did you write this letter?"

"I wrote it the day you left to visit Santa Monica. Didn't I date it?"

"No." I continue reading the letter, and Mom continues reading her book or pretending to.

I purchased a gun for protection after one of the many times he beat me. With each beating, I was more and more terrified for my life and yours, but I was more afraid I would use the gun. I wanted to get it out of our house but had nowhere to take it.

One evening, I met with a long-time friend from work who agreed to purchase the gun from me. You and I walked to the local tavern to meet John. It was around 8:00 p.m. When we arrived, I saw him sitting near the pool table in the rear of the bar. I bought you a Shirley Temple and me a drink, and we joined him and his wife. I hadn't laid my handbag down or taken a sip of my drink before all hell broke loose.

I had my back to the door and didn't see the man approach the table until it was too late. My chair was kicked out from under me, knocking me to the floor, and it was while lying on the floor and looking up that I realized it was Dahmon.

I gasp loudly, holding my hand over my mouth. My eyes search Mom's face to witness her response to my own. She is emotionless. She turns her head back to her book. Getting up from the chair, I turn and lay the letter down before grabbing a tissue and excusing myself to the bathroom. Attempting to compose myself not to hurt her further, I splash water on my face and return. I sit down, place my hands on the arms of the chair, and stretch my back against it. I roll my neck and feel the baby kick—a new life I will protect with my own if necessary. I pick up the letter and continue, beginning a few lines up from where I left to ensure I read it correctly.

I reached for you because I thought you were the reason he came back. He said nothing. Once the initial shock wore off that he was alive and there, I knew what he wanted. I knew I would die, and I thought I would die in front of you. I crawled under the pool table with my handbag and screamed for someone to get my child out. My friend, John, fought with him. I could hear several other men in the bar as they attempted to calm him down but failed. I could see the feet moving around and hear yelling. I searched for little feet but couldn't find you. Still, to this day, I don't know where you were at this point. I saw a giant hand reach under the table and felt the pain as I was pulled out from under by my hair. I pulled the gun out of my bag; I pulled the trigger as he pulled me up.

The .22 caliber hit Dahmon in the heart; he staggered backward with my hair in his hands, pulling me down on top of him. They said he was dead before he hit the floor. I laid across him and cried. That's all I remember. I don't know where you were. I didn't see nor remember the police coming in or taking me away.

When I was a little girl, I heard a sermon, and the preacher said that every sin a person commits is a drop of blood on a white page. "My book is all red" are the only words I spoke after the incident. It was an accident, but it happened. I remained under sedation and suicide watch for weeks. Eventually, the shock wore off, and so did the suicidal thoughts, and I was charged with his death and taken to jail.

"Mom, is this why we never attended church when I was young?" I ask as she nods yes. I continue to read.

You hadn't been out of the hospital long and still had little to

234

no memory, and you were placed in foster care. You didn't even know who I was before or after this happened. The doctors said you quit talking, and the entire time you were in foster care, you didn't speak. I know you have no memory of all of this, so I didn't want you to know it. I'm sorry, Dahlia. I wanted to protect you. I knew what you saw when you called me from England, asking why you would have repressed memories, especially the darkness.

Again, I can't read this with your eyes, but please consider what I've said. I know you will be upset that I didn't tell you this part of the story seven years ago when I told you about the kidnapping, near-drowning, and amnesia, but Dahlia, I am sure you are aware there are just things we want to bury, and some things that need to stay in the abyss.

I love you with my whole heart, Mom.

She wrote this letter recently after my last visit to see her. Mom's words, a drop of blood on a white page, echo in my ears as I remember the red dot on the white ceiling that changed my life. Mom's hair was pulled, pulling her forward as he fell, reminding me of what happened with Derek. I feel these words. I feel the terror of the moment. This could've easily happened to me. The angry words that spewed from Kimberly's mouth weren't told with this letter's raw emotion and knowledge. No one but Mom can tell what Dahmon did to her and what she endured to protect her life and mine. I glance over the top of the letter and watch my mother closely as she holds her book as steady as possible. It's heartbreaking to watch her fight to do a simple task such as reading a book, and I wonder how many times she suffered head injuries at the hands of the man she was married to. Her calm and cheerful attitude makes me feel ashamed. She handles what life has thrown at her with a smile.

"For me? You were willing and able to do that for me?" I ask, and Mom nods her head and stares into my face for a reaction. I give her an honest one. "Why didn't you protect me from Bob? You held on to all these secrets as if they were a thing of value." Now, sitting beside my mother, I place my hand over her heart; then, I reach out to hold her shaking hands in mine.

When she looks at me, I think I might be seeing my mother fully for the first time. "Killing a man, even accidentally, Dahlia isn't something that is easily forgotten. It isn't something a person willingly shares. I wanted to forget how he almost killed you, tortured me, and nearly killed me multiple times. Did you ever wonder why I lost my fight? You've told me I failed to protect you. I had nothing left inside of me to protect either of us. So, I quit fighting. Do you remember the day Bob knocked you into the side of the truck? Do you remember getting up, then he hit you again and again until you couldn't get up?"

"Of course, I do. Only one of many bad memories."

"Try doing that with a baby in your arms and a hole in your head. Every time I thought of the day Dahmon died, I pushed it out of my mind, and I was fortunate enough to bury it until now. I buried the pain along with his body. It's incredible what the mind can block. You blocked out nearly seven years. So, yes, I do see a value in that. But when your name was revealed, I knew it was only a matter of time before this would come out."

I reach for my mother, and I hold her in my arms. No more words need ever be spoken on the matter. "Mom, I'm happy I didn't get this letter after you died. That would've been awful."

"I see your point."

"Did you know about Kimberly? Did you know Dahmon had another child?"

"No, I suspected he cheated on me with all his travels, but I had no idea about a child."

"Mom, I will go back and fix this with Roland if you come

with me to New York and then to Scotland." Mom nods her head, "Deal."

"That was quick. What has changed your mind?"

"I could've lost you, Dahlia. You're getting ready to have my grandchild, and I am hopeful you will marry Roland, and I can't miss that." Crying while we hang on to each other and rock back and forth, I swear I am having my tear ducts removed after this child is born.

Later leaning on the kitchen island while on the phone making plans for Mom and me to travel, I pull open a drawer to find an ink pen; instead, I find the gun I purchased—no wonder she didn't want it in the house. I place the gun in the glove compartment of my rental car, realizing I need to get rid of it. I don't think Mom knows about Bob's involvement in my kidnapping or Kimberly's death, but I don't trust him not to hurt either of us.

Chapter 20

Praying

The following morning, at the nearly finished lake house, I wander through its emptiness, running my hands along the unpainted walls. The idea of building a home on the same property my mother lives sinks in, and I laugh as I tell myself, "You've come a long way." Standing on the second floor, looking out the glass wall, I see a boulder. Hurrying down the stairs and exiting the back of the house, I step out on the temporary boards creating a bridge over the holes dug before pouring the concrete footings for a deck. I carefully make my way toward the boulder recently placed, looking out over the lake. I touch it as I circle to the front and see an engraved plaque, "Dahlia's Thinking Spot." I run my fingers over the image of the praying hands. I glance toward Mom's house before climbing on top of the boulder, and unlike all the times before, I leave, not knowing what course of action I should take.

Meandering up the hill, I admire the property's beauty, the flowers that Mom has planted, and the different varieties of palm trees. It looks like a tropical jungle. Instead of going into the house, I stick my head in the back door and yell at Mom, "I will be back in a bit."

Roger follows close behind. "I'll be going alone this time."

"Ma'am, that isn't a good idea. You need to let me drive you."

"It won't be the first bad idea I've ever had. Take the day off, Roger. Go sight-seeing. I need to be alone."

Honestly, I have no particular path in mind as I drive mindlessly and replay the turn of events, what Mom has gone through, and what I have learned to be the reasons. Not sure if it was mindful or mindless driving, but I park across the street from Bob's house. While sitting here, the hatred running through my veins shocks even me. I've never hated anyone. The images of all the years play out in front of me like a movie. No one else will hurt me or my mother or my unborn child. He prepares his boat for what appears to be a fishing trip. I'll never forgive what he set in motion. I'll never forgive him for the paranoid person he has forced me to be. Why should he wander this earth not concerned with who wants to hurt him? I'm not going just to sit here and be a stalker.

I have something to say. I don't know what it is exactly, but I'm here, so I might as well say it to his face. Grabbing a handful of hair, I tuck it under my cap while pulling it down further on my head. As I cross the street, I keep my head down. It doesn't make much difference; it's a sunny morning, and several neighbors are out. I'm going to say what I have to say, and then I'll be gone. After giving a brief rap at the door, I immediately step off the porch as words dance around in my head. I want him to know that I know everything he's done.

The door opens, and I lift my head and eyes to meet his. "What do you want? You need to leave and get off my property." Bob demands as he steps off the porch and toward me. His back straightens, he puffs his chest out and looks me up and down. His eyes stop on my pregnant belly. He's close enough I can smell the whiskey on his breath. I instinctively wrap my arms around my baby to protect its innocence.

"Your plan failed. Kimberly is dead, and it's your fault. Did you ever ask Mom what happened to her after discovering how Dahmon died? Did you ever love her? There is no way you could and used something so tragic against her and me." Speaking in a calm voice, I search for answers and wait for a reaction of any kind, but he gives none. He doesn't deny anything either.

He slithers past me and carries a small cooler to his boat reaching over the side and placing it inside. He turns, "If you want to continue talking, speed it up because I'm leaving. You have a lot of nerve talking to me about talking to someone. Did you talk to me before you wrote it all in the pages of your book?"

"I tried twice to talk to you and beg you to leave me alone, but the scar on your leg reminds me of how that turned out. I'm done. I have nothing else to add." I turn to leave.

"Are you? I seriously doubt that."

Turning again, "I see you're leaving. You're taking a night fishing trip to the river."

"Aren't you observant? Don't you want to know why Dahlia?"

"Why you're fishing? No, I don't give a rat's ass. Why you've done the things you've done, of course, I do. I want to know why you've done everything you've ever done, except I know the answer. You're pure evil, Bob."

He stops checking the hitch, securing items in the boat and faces me. "Evil. I supposed you would see it that way. I love your mother and tried to love you and be a father to you. I deserve some compensation for my efforts."

I didn't come here with a plan. I leave but turn back to face him, "Well, you have a shitty way of showing you loved her, and you were no father. I know why, pure greed and lust for things you couldn't have." I'm labored with anxiety and anger. My hands are shaking. "You'll die by my hand, Bob. I promise you that."

"Like mother, like daughter." He states loudly and smirks. He searches my face for a reaction, but I give none. He continues, "Before my days are up, I assure you there will be a cost for your truth. I'm not finished with you yet."

"Is that a threat?" I ask, and he smiles.

"Does it sound like one?" Bob only stares. I hope he knows his dirty deeds have caught up with his black soul, but if he doesn't, I will remind him. I turn hastily and leave before I pick up something and bash him in the head. When I reach my car, I am shaking, not because I'm scared, but because I'm angry. I drive a mile and pull over. My insides are shaking worse than what is evident by my hands. I make a call, "Hey, what are you doing?"

"Nothing."

"Can we talk?"

* * *

Several hours later, driving through a well-needed downpour, I pull into the driveway at Mom's house. Then the rain just stops. When I step out of the vehicle and look toward the setting sun slightly hidden behind the storm clouds, I grasp the symbolism. *The storm is finished.*

"What did you say, ma'am?" Roger is standing near my car to assist me. "Are you all right, ma'am?"

"Yes, thank you. Mom hasn't arrived home yet?"

"You're wet and covered in dirt. Did something happen?"

"I got out of the car to check my tire. It's nothing. A little rain and dirt never hurt anyone."

D.F. Kennedy

"If you say so, ma'am. I don't know where your mother is. I did what you told me to do and took the day off. When I got back, you were both gone."

I call her twice, and Mom finally answers, "I'm almost there."

"Okay, pull into the garage. I'll be waiting there for you."

"Roger, she is almost home. Thank you and enjoy the rest of your night. We'll both be home." I kick off my dirty shoes, enter the garage, and place them in the laundry basket. When Mom pulls into the garage and closes the door, I hand her a robe, take her muddy clothes and shoes, and put them in the basket. I hug her trembling body and send her inside to shower. "I'll meet you in the living room. It's going to be fine, I promise." Mom doesn't speak. She does what I ask her to do.

I strip out of my clothes in the guest bathroom and put them in the same basket. I turn on the shower to steam the room like I always do to cleanse the toxins. I select my "Whisky Girl" playlist and turn the volume up to hear it over the cascading water and the noise in my head. I've revealed no emotion to the day's events. I know I have to be strong—I slide down the wall, sit on the shower floor, let the water beat against me and wash away my sins. The song, The River and Me by Tim McGraw plays, I can't laugh, and I can't cry. I've done unto others as I would have them do unto me, but I've stepped off the ledge to walk on the insane side this time.

Chapter 21

Consequences

The look on Bob's face when I fought back was priceless. He created this version of me, and I don't like it. Bitterness and anger will turn me into someone like him, and he'll win. I can't allow that.

Mom and I sit quietly in her living room, waiting for the Bond premiere to begin. She appears subdued as she stares off into space and is deep in thought.

There have been many new photos of Roland posted to his social media pages, and it appears his life has gone on without skipping a beat. I left a congratulatory message on his voicemail, but I've not heard from him. I had no idea I'd be in California during his premiere and now I wish I'd said I would attend with him. I don't want to cry or appear weak again, especially around Roland, so it's for the best I didn't go. And after today's events, I need to push him as far from me as possible. However, I wouldn't miss his big moment.

When the premiere goes live on Mom's television, she smiles and is overly excited to see Roland as the camera pans to him. He exits the vehicle and steps out on the red carpet, and I sharply inhale as he buttons his jacket and waves. We watch him glide from spot to spot, dressed in his perfectly fitted black tux; he smiles as the cameras love him. The reporters call out his name, and he turns and poses for each photo. When he is asked a question about the film and speaks, his voice comforts me. It seems like such a long time since I heard his voice. My heart skips, and I feel the baby flutter in my belly.

The warm feelings are replaced with an unwelcome tension as a woman, not a co-star, puts her arm around his waist and smiles for the camera. She intends to be photographed with him, and I can't help but feel jealous. I should be with him. It should be me on his arm. But she appears to be stepping into my shoes or wants to be. Wait, she looks familiar. She's the same brunette he was photographed having lunch with him a while back. "Did he take a date to his premiere?"

"Dahlia, it's nothing," Mom assures me.

Looking down, noticing my nails digging into the coffee table, I release the table and sit back against the couch. "In the grand scheme of things, Mom, it is definitely nothing." As if reading my mind, Roland reaches around to remove her arm from his waist and her hand from his ass. He frowns and mumbles something in her direction.

The interviewer mentions my name and asks a question I didn't hear, but Roland's response is clear, "Dahlia is well and enjoying time away from the spotlight while she masters the art of pregnancy. She's more beautiful than I have ever seen her."

"It's rumored you and Ms. Frost have called it quits. Can you respond to that rumor?"

The brunette still standing near him smiles. Roland's smile fades only for a second, and I think he will turn away from the camera, but instead, he smiles that fake smile of his, the one where he smirks and his lips are tilted. "What are you doing? Are you asking me about this tonight? I thought we were here to talk about the new Bond movie." He turns away from the camera but turns back. "Look, don't believe rumors. Dahlia went through a traumatic event; the press let the world know of her kidnapping, inheritance, and name. Couples don't call it quits when they love each other and have a child or are about to have a child. They do anything and everything to help the other through something so traumatic." He turns from the camera.

I excuse myself for the night and feel Mom's eyes on me as I leave the room. "Good night, Mom. I swear it will all be set right."

"Oh, I have no doubt, Dahlia. It always is," Mom assures me.

For someone who hates social media, I have come to rely on it to keep tabs on Roland and to pay attention to the comments that have not gone away. I still see comments from forevermrshughes, although Roland is adored now that I am not in the photos. As I scroll the sites, I lay in bed, nurse my jaw and pride. After my kidnapping, when I left Scotland, there were reports of Roland and I breaking up. Old photos of Roland with other women were found in some archives and posted as new events. There are photos of me from the other day, pregnant, walking into stores with my bodyguard, rumored to be my baby's daddy. I stop scrolling.

Three hours later, unable to sleep and missing him terribly, I can't take it anymore—I text him. I know he's better off without me, and I should leave him alone, but I'm unable. He owns my thoughts.

Me
Congratulations

I watch the three dots appear, and I am happy to know he is holding his phone and thinking of me. Picturing a tether, I wish I could pull him through the phone and into my arms.

Roland
Thank you. How are you and the baby?

Me
We're good.
I left you a voicemail this a.m.
Mom and I watched you tonight.
I am so proud of you, and I miss you.

Roland
That's great news. You should've been here with me—on my arm, and it would have been more enjoyable.

Me
I would have if I knew I'd only be 1 1/2 hrs from you. We need to talk. Can I see you before you leave?

Roland
Tell me when and where. @ Moms? 🖤

Me
🏴 Yes. Tomorrow morning?

Roland
See you then.

Since the kidnapping, I hate being alone, and thankfully, I've not had to be since returning from Scotland. I tossed and turned for several more hours but eventually drifted off. When a light tap on the bedroom window startles me, I quickly shut off the light and pull back the curtain to see Roland's face staring at me and his hand waving. I motion for him to come to the door.

Opening the door, he steps inside, and I punch him in the gut. "You scared the bejeezus out of me. What were you thinking?"

Roland reaches out and pulls me into him. "I'm sorry. I wanted to surprise you. I didn't want to wake your mother." He kicks off his muddy shoes.

"Too late for that," Mom walks up behind me, smiling like she has a secret. "So happy to see you, dear. I told Roger you were coming; he didn't give you a problem, did he?"

I sigh and shake my head. I should've known no one would get past Roger unless he were briefed beforehand. She squeezes in between us and hugs Roland around his waist.

"Good night. Love you both. We can visit in the morning." She taps my arm as she passes me. "Be nice, Dahlia."

I roll my eyes. "Not that I am not grateful to see you, but why did you drive here tonight? You should've waited until morning. She called you, didn't she?" I shut and locked the door behind him.

"No, I called her for directions, I forgot, and these roads out here in the dark all look eerie. Isn't it obvious why I came tonight, Whisky Girl? I had to see you and didn't want to wait until morning."

I pull him into the guest bedroom, "Are you going to be angry that I want to go back to bed?" I tease.

"Absolutely not," he answers as I step toward him and help unbutton his shirt. I push it over his shoulders and down his long arms to the floor. With both hands, I pull his t-shirt out of his jeans and guide it over his head as he bends lower. I throw it to the floor. Then I place my hand over the recently received red scar gunshot wound and remember that he was willing to sacrifice his life for me. I release his belt and unbutton his jeans. I take my hands on each side of his hips and slither his jeans down his legs, bending down with them. Roland steps out of his jeans and briefs. I reach up, so Roland can help pull me up. He leans in and kisses me. "I don't want to touch you, love. I need to shower first. Is that all right?"

"Of course."

"I had to change a flat tire on my way here. That was a hell of a downpour earlier, wasn't it?"

"Yes, it was. Do you want me to join you in the shower?" I ask while picking up his damp clothes.

"I'd love that, but not tonight. Wait for me, and don't move or undress; I want to do that."

After his shower, I am again consumed with him. He lifts my nightgown over my head and is pleased to see I have nothing on under it. I'm standing before him, hoping he can see my heart. Down on his knees, he places his hands on my belly and kisses it. I reach down and run my fingers through his damp hair. At the same time, his eyes search for mine, and I see his tears. My heart shatters into a million pieces knowing the pain I have caused him.

Crawling into bed and lying in each other's arms, I say, "Roland, I want to apologize for leaving you in Scotland."

"Shhh, we're not talking of such things tonight." We whisper sweet words but speak of nothing outside this room, this bed. "I have missed you, Whisky Girl. I just want to love you."

I can hardly breathe as my lungs fill with passion instead of air. My hands search his body, reassuring myself and him that I am his, and he is mine. Our bodies meld as we love each other until the sun comes up and we are both exhausted. I moan loudly as my body collapses on his.

"Shhhh, you'll wake your mother."

"She told me to be nice."

He pulls in close to spoon me. I'm almost asleep when I hear him humming, barely above a whisper. He's the gentlest person I have ever known. His song lulls me to sleep. Only three hours later, we are awakened by noise from the kitchen and the smell of bacon. For the first time since my kidnapping, I feel safe. I feel loved. I roll over and move into him as close as I can get. He is watching me and squeezes me gently. "I love you."

"I love you, too," I whisper. Then I say it louder, "I love you, too. Roland."

He releases me and sits up in bed. "You've not said those words to me for thirteen years. I thought I'd never hear those words leave your mouth again, let alone touch you."

"I love you—always have, and I always will. I need to tell you something else, and I need you to commit this to memory just in case I don't get to tell you how much every day for the rest of our lives."

"All right?"

I sit in bed and lean against the headboard, pulling the covers around my chest. I pat them down, tucking them around my legs. "You do love the most." I turn my head to look into his face. "You also know how to show love the best. I've lived my entire life dead other than the times you've participated in it. I remained invisible until you returned to me and breathed life into my hollowness." A single tear escapes me, but before I can wipe it away, Roland twists his body to sit on his knees, facing me; he wipes it away with his thumb. I place my hand on his chest and over his heart before continuing, "I only thought I was healed and happy while alone in my tower, and I'm sorry that loving me has consequences. I told you I regretted being the one who loved the most, but I was wrong; it's you. Do you forgive me?"

"You've done nothing to be forgiven for. There are good and bad consequences for everything we do and say, but you must commit something to memory, too."

"What is that?"

"Forever is a long time, and I'm willing to do forever with you, but no more running away. I've always known I love you more."

"I've done much to be forgiven for, Roland. I didn't say that. I said you love the best. You know how to give love better. I am still sure I love you more."

Dressed, we meet Mom in the kitchen, enjoy breakfast together, and catch up on all our news before Roger taps on the kitchen door, "Ma'am, there is a sheriff here to see you and your mother."

"Let him in," I respond.

A man of average height with muscles as large as Roland's steps through the door and removes his hat. "I am Sheriff McMillen from the Santa Barbara Sheriff's office. I am here to see Mrs. Richardson," the sheriff says.

"Mom."

"Yes, I heard. Please sit down, sheriff, and don't mind the breakfast mess; it is awful early for a house call. What can I do for you?" Mom sits back in her chair and pushes her breakfast plate away. I sit on Roland's knee.

The sheriff reaches over and shakes my hand as we introduce ourselves, then he does the same to Roland. "Nice to meet you, Mr. Hughes."

The sheriff watches Mom closely before speaking and looks at me. I'm assuming he has noticed her shaking. "She is fine; go ahead, sir," I tell him.

"Ma'am, your husband has been reported missing by his neighbor. Upon investigation, his boat was spotted floating near the Santa Ynez River without an occupant. His vehicle and boat trailer is still parked. Does he know how to swim?"

Mom gasps and nods her head yes. The sheriff continues, "We've gone to his residence to ensure he didn't let someone else borrow the truck and boat, but he wasn't there. We have searched the river banks and haven't located a body. The search is ongoing, but he could have been washed out into the ocean by now if he fell overboard."

"I guess in California, a person doesn't have to be gone at least twenty-four hours to be considered a missing person? There isn't a body?" I want to know and ask more aggressively than I should have.

"He's missing, not technically a missing person. As I mentioned, we believe he fell overboard. It is being decided if the river should be dragged, but because of where the boat was located, the Santa Ynez River flows east to west and empties into the ocean; the body could be anywhere." He continues talking to Mom, "I understand you and Mr. Richardson are separated but still legally married, and you and your daughter are his only kin." Mom is oddly quiet. I feel it best to keep my mouth shut, so I offer Mom my hand, and even that feels forced. I clear breakfast dishes off the table while the sheriff steps outside to take a phone call. No words are spoken between Mom, Roland, and me as we glance at each other.

The sheriff comes back in and sits down. "Sheriff, what happens now?" Mom asks. I sit beside her, reach for her hand again, gently shaking my head and watching the sheriff, hinting to ignore her confusion.

"Well, ma'am, that is another reason I came to see you two ladies in person. I need to know where you both were last night and early this morning. Neighbors have reported seeing each of you near his home, if not at his home, yesterday. Let's start with you, Ms. Frost. You were seen first standing at his door and speaking to him." Mom and Roland are staring at me.

"Yes, I drove to his house, knocked on his door, and when he answered, I told him I knew he was the one behind my kidnapping."

"Was that all you said?"

"Yes, if the neighbor was watching, they saw me walk away seconds later."

"What about you, Mrs. Richardson? You were seen arriving after your daughter left, and apparently, you went inside."

"Yes, I drove there yesterday, as well. After her traumatic kidnapping, Dahlia came home to see me only the day before yesterday. She and I agreed to go to Scotland to be near Roland so that she could have the baby there, and I wouldn't be far from her. I told Bob I was filing for divorce before I left, so expect that. I wanted to say what I needed to say to his face. I thought you and your office would have him in jail before now."

"The kidnapping is an international case, and it will take some time and a lot of paperwork and legwork to charge him with conspiracy. And the person accusing him is dead. It is in the works, but that is a different matter than why I am here." Sheriff McMillen writes more information on his paper. "What time were you both there, and what time did you leave?" he asks. He wants details of my kidnapping, and I tell him the entire story and how Bob was involved. "I'm so sorry that happened to you, ma'am. However, that does give you a powerful motive to want him dead."

"Does it? Well, you said you don't know if he is dead. I thought he was only a missing person, right?"

He turns his head from me and directs his attention toward Roland. "Mr. Hughes, were you here last evening?"

"I was in Hollywood all evening in front of thousands of

people and cameras; then I went back to my hotel. I drove here this morning to see my fiancé and Sylvia."

"I presume you all will provide proof."

"Of course."

"What about you, Ms. Frost?"

"What about me? Provide proof of what? He was alive when I was last seen leaving?" I stare at the sheriff. "If you want me to tell you I'm sorry he is missing, I can't." I watch Mom and Roland shake their head simultaneously and give me faces to shut up. "Well, I'm not, but I was long gone before he drove away to go fishing." I stand before continuing. "We're done answering questions. If you need to ask anything else, call my attorney." I hand him one of my attorney's business cards. "I'm sorry you have a mess on your hands, but that sick bastard had more enemies than me, and he was devious in his dealings. If he didn't die by accident, you need to dig into his dealings thoroughly. He probably staged his death so that you would think I did it. Read my book; there is no love lost between us. If he has conspired, maybe someone will be able to prove that. One thing I know, he's smarter than I ever gave him credit for being."

"Have a good day. I'll be in touch," he says to Mom as he leaves. He smirks at me as he goes.

The kitchen smells of secrecy with a hint of bacon. Both Roland's and Mom's eyes search mine. I hold my hands in the air. "What? I didn't do anything," I attempt to offer assurance. I keep busy loading the dishwasher as we discuss this tragedy if it is indeed a tragedy. However, not one of us asked the other if we were involved in something sinister.

"No one in this house did anything wrong. We were all where we said we were when we said we were there." I state, and Roland and Mom both agree.

We step outside to enjoy the weather. Sitting in the swing with my legs folded under me, Roland uses his long legs to rock the swing back and forth while resting his head against the back. "So, did I understand Sylvia to say that you and she are moving to Scotland?"

My head is resting on his shoulder, or was, I jerk my head, cover my mouth with my hands, and smile. "I supposed I should ask you if that is all right with you? Mom and I discussed everything we needed the first day I got here, and I told her I would come back if she came with me. I was afraid Bob would try to do something to her to get to me after the kidnapping, but I don't have to worry about that anymore. But she wants to go. Would it be all right with you if we moved in with you? Or I could get us our own place."

Roland cups my cheeks with both hands and pulls my face to meet his. "I am so happy."

Sitting in the glider beside us, Mom begins to cry, so I ask her, "Are you okay, Mom? Is it Bob? Roland said we can go, so it can't be that."

"Dahlia, an awful lot has happened in a few short months. You and Roland, the stalking, me and Bob, the kidnapping and finding out Bob was behind it. It's just a lot. Will you grab me Kleenex, Dahlia?"

"Yes, of course."

"Tell her, or I will."

"Tell me what?" I ask as I step back outside and hand Mom the tissue. Roland is standing near Mom looking down at her, but quickly turns his attention to me. Searching both their faces, I wait for someone to answer me.

"Roland has something he needs to tell you," Mom speaks loud and quickly.

Roland smirks at Sylvia, then back at me before he reaches into the pocket of his jeans, bends down on one knee in front of me, and picks up my left hand. "Whisky Girl, will—?" Jumping up, I answer before he can finish asking.

"Yes, I can't believe you have my ring with you. You don't need to ask me twice. I said yes, and I meant it. I just needed some time to get my mind and heart right." I touch his heart with my right hand, and Roland slides my engagement ring back on my left finger. He then puts his ring back on his right ring finger.

"Promise me; you won't ever take this ring off again."

"I won't." I nod in agreement and wrap my arms around his neck. He picks me up and sits me on his lap, where I rest my head against his chest and listen to his perfect heartbeat in rhythm with mine.

The following morning, standing with his car door open, Roland prepares to return to LA. Standing beside him, holding hands, not wanting to let go of him, he kisses my cheek. Then he steps back and tilts my chin up before commenting, "What happened to your face?"

Mom is waving goodbye to him from the patio. Reluctantly I let go and step back. "I smacked it with the car door when I got in." He laughs and kisses me again before climbing into the driver's seat and starting the engine. As he prepares to leave, a car pulls up behind him. I watch as he looks in the rearview mirror, puts the car in park, steps out, waves Roger off, and meets the driver himself.

Stepping quickly, I reach Mom's side, curious about who it is, "Do you know the car?" I ask.

"I don't recognize the car or the young man." The driver steps out, walks to the passenger side of his car, lifts out a bouquet of black dahlias, and turns to face Roland. Roland grabs the young man shoving him up against the vehicle. What happens next is fast, and I scarcely believe it as the vase shatters and flowers spill. At the same time, Roger runs to stand in front of me; I hear a gasp behind me. I twist around to see Mom fall to the ground.

"Mom, are you all right?" I scream, "Call an ambulance." Kneeling beside her, she attempts to speak, but her words are slurred and intermittent.

Barely above a whisper, she sputters, "Tell...you... WHOLE TRUTH." She becomes unresponsive.

THE END

I hope you enjoyed The Truth, the first book in the So Help Me God Series.

I'm a new Indie author. I don't have a huge following or any of the marketing techniques I've been told are needed to be successful. It's a good thing I don't listen to what I'm told.

If you enjoyed The Truth, please leave a review and recommend my novel to your friends.

I hope you look forward to The Whole Truth, the second book in the series, as I look forward to writing it.

Best Wishes,

DF Kennedy

Author's Note

Hello,

Imagine sitting across from each other and having a wee whisky, coffee, or tea, if you prefer. I want to get to know you, and I want you to know me.

When I sat down at my desk and placed my fingers on the keys to begin the arduous task of writing a memoir, I was overwhelmed like my mother before me. Weeks passed as I typed thousands of words only to erase them the following day.

I had a breakthrough when I was inspired to write fiction. The words poured out of me as I safely tucked my and my mother's stories into these fictitious characters. I tell stories she and I have wanted to share for a long time but couldn't get out of our heads and onto the paper. The depth of dysfunction, bad choices, abuse, and heaviness felt lighter as I covered it in a candy-coated romance that celebrates what is good in the world, faith, hope, love, and forgiveness, to name only a few. And, of course, a fictitious mystery.

Many have asked which stories are genuine? My answer is if I wanted to tell true stories, I'd have written a memoir. I will say actual events inspired this novel, but nothing is written precisely as it happened.

If you or anyone you know suffers from abuse, please seek help. There are many organizations available to assist. I have listed some resources on the front pages.

I can't read this with your eyes, but I hope you take one

thing away from it after it is finished, you are never stuck, and we all deserve happiness. Whatever that looks like.

All My Best,
Donna
linktr.ee/donna_kennedy

Whisky Girl Playlist

I thought I was unique when I created a playlist on
Spotify to incorporate with my novels.
I have discovered that many authors use their love of
music to bring out their creativity. Each chapter heading
is a song title on the *Whisky Girl Playlist*. Search DF
Kennedy Author/Whisky Girl.

I highly recommend downloading Spotify and listening
to the titles to feel the full effect of the chapters,
especially while road-tripping, as Dahlia mentions
in *The Truth*.

The Truth..Jason Aldean
I'm Like A Bird............................... Nellie Furtado
Everything I wanted........................Billie Ellish
Whiskey Girl....................................Toby Keith
Dare ya...Carly Pearce
All the Whiskey in the World...........Carly Pearce
Empire State of Mind.......................Jay-Z, Alicia Keys
Read All About It.............................Emeli Sande

Family Portrait................................Pink
Nightmare...Halsey
Piece by Piece..................................Kelly Clarkson
Stay..Rihanna, Mikky Ekko
To Be Loved.....................................Adele
Malibu...Miley Cirus
Lover, Lover.....................................Jerod Neiman
A Scary Time....................................Lynzy Lab
The Story..Brandi Carlile
Skyfall...Adele
Somebody's Watching Me...............Rockwell
Unless it's With you........................Christina Aguilera
Secrets...Pink
Sorry..Halsey
Elastic Heart....................................Sia
Skyscraper..Demi Lavato
Easy on Me   ....Adele
Praying   ....Kesha
Consequences..................................Camila Cabello
Helium..Sia

Made in the USA
Monee, IL
30 January 2023

2481becc-b260-42ce-926b-c10221effc5bR01